WHAT IT MEANS TO BE A GROWN-UP

THE COMPLETE
AND
DEFINITIVE ANSWER

edited by JOSEPH FINK

COMMONPLACE BOOKS
BROOKLYN, NY

Visit **www.commonplacebooks.com** for more information about this book and other projects. Please send any comments or questions to **joseph@commonplacebooks.com**

Cover design by Justin Marquis

www.scrollingmarquis.com

ISBN 978-0-9852060-0-0

Published by Commonplace Books

Brooklyn, NY

Printed by Sterling Pierce Co., Inc. in Queens.

We recommend them for any book printing needs.

First edition.

for my father, the first artist I ever knew

Also available from Commonplace Books

A Commonplace Book of the Weird: The Untold Stories of H. P. Lovecraft

CONTENTS

INTRODUCTION

BY JOSEPH FINK

In the couple years I spent making this book, I had the same conversation with many people.

"So, what are you working on?"

"A book about what it means to be a grown-up."

"Oh. Well, could you let me know when you find out?"

I had this conversation with college students, and I had it with members of AARP. What interested me wasn't just that none of them knew. It was that none of them knew despite the fact that they all wanted to find out. All of them seemed to be hoping that I actually would stumble across the answer while making this book.

And I have. Didn't you read the cover?

The idea behind this book was a simple one. I asked writers from all over the country to create pieces that considered the question, "What does it mean to be a grown-up?" The results came in a dizzying variety: fiction and non-fiction, prose and poetry, and even a couple plays. While the idea was simple, the question clearly was not.

In one sense, the definition of "grown-up" should be easy. Our bodies get old. We were children once. Now we are something else. But that doesn't feel like enough to us. If being a grown-up was merely a matter of time spent alive, where would the accomplishment be? What would we have earned by achieving adulthood?

These days, children carry phones. Men in their forties play video games. Women in their fifties eagerly await a movie made for children. I don't think that any of that is necessarily bad. But it is a crisis. We live now in a crisis of grown-up-ness. We have lost any sense of what it could mean.

Even as this book is being released, a new batch of college graduates are entering the adult world. It is likely that many of them thought, when starting college, that they would leave it feeling like a grown-up, or at least knowing what that meant. It is unlikely that any of them feel that way now.

But here's the truth: being a grown-up means whatever we all decide it means. It is an idea defined by cultural context, and we are, all of us, that context. So this book is us, a community and a culture, getting together to define "grown-up."

You can flip through the book looking for the one page with the answer, but it doesn't exist in one word, or one sentence, or one page. The book in its entirety is the answer.

While I was working on this book, my father died at the age of 56. He had been struggling with heart disease for years, and yet his death was a shattering surprise to his family. Like a lot of things in life, it was both long expected and completely out of the blue. It was inevitable, and it was impossible.

And, ultimately, looking at all the different answers in this book, I think I can say two things about being a grown-up for certain. Being a grown-up is inevitable. Being a grown-up is impossible.

Good luck.

WHAT DOES IT MEAN TO BE A GROWN-UP?

"For that indeed is what becoming an adult is all about. Gradually, doors of opportunity close to you as you choose your path as an adult toward mortality. That's how I look at life anyway."

—*John Hodgman, the Judge John Hodgeman Podcast*

"It means recognizing your temporal limitations (thinking about and respecting death).

It means recognizing the interconnectedness of all things (thinking about and respecting other people)."

—*Regis, 33, writer*

"Being a grown-up means realizing you can buy candy whenever you want, but you don't want candy."

—*Kevin, 28, software developer*

SUM OF ITS PARTS

Talk loudly
Walk with my head held high
Listen intently with my head tilted
Put one hand in my pocket
Hold one arm bent at elbow with wrist slack
Talk with my hands
Am physically and practically flexible
Use the wrong word confidently in conversation
Have boundless enthusiasm
Sing in the car
Criticize
Get carsick
Get along with teenagers
Like talking on phone
Get claustrophobic

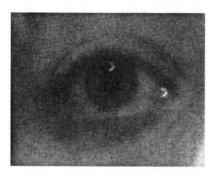

Vote Democrat
Only vote in major elections
Do not wear pastels
Get colds easily
Don't eat enough fruit or vegetables
Tune out of conversations because I'm thinking
of other things
Lose wallets
Need a big blanket at night
Wear big earrings
Teach with a "teacher voice"
Always wear lipstick
Look weird with eye shadow
Drive nervously
Brake quickly

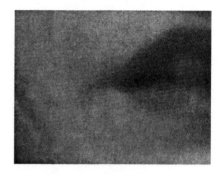

Pee frequently
Bite people as a child
Show off my legs
Hold a glass under the sink, pour water out of the
glass several times before I drink the water
Answer phone in pitched-up voice
Do headstands
Drink coffee before bedtime
Shave
Sit down in the shower
Wear the same clothes
Dress funkily
Refer to pantyhose as "nylons"
Wear nylons without underwear
Call my mother "ma"

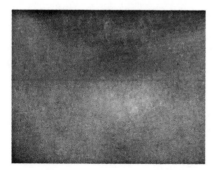

things I do like my mother

BY JACQUELYN LANDGRAF

Hold liquid in my mouth for very long periods of
time
Fall silent for hours
Smoke
Have a quick temper
Scratch my head
Stand still, stare at a fixed point
Am ultimately pretty zen
Remember numbers and dates
Shake hands
Eat enormous quantities of food with little
consequence
Poke fun at my mother
Like drinking

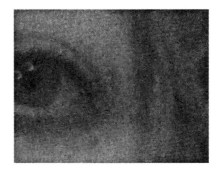

Am a very good Samaritan
Like mushrooms
Eat seafood
Love the ocean
Feel wary of politics and religion
Swim like a fish
Wear glasses and contacts
Keep busy
Jump cars
Like showers better than baths
Am nostalgic
Have dry skin
Listen well
Work with my hands

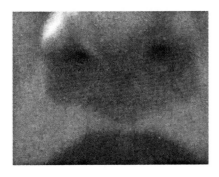

Play in the snow
Have a wild streak
Work hard
Not complain
Draw well
Drink coffee before bedtime
Laugh deeply
Cry easily
Cry when I laugh
Choke on things
Interject conversations with humor that I find
funny and causes people to laugh politely
Clear my throat
Sleep on my back

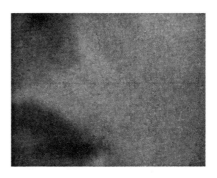

things I do like my father

ROCKSTAR

BY DANIEL McCOY

1

Twenty years ago, give or take, you were a rock star.

You were in high school, and you were picking up the bass guitar for the first time. Your friends were learning the drums, the guitar. Playing in someone's basement felt like being in a studio. You all pretty much sucked, though some of you were getting better. Names like Claypool, Flea, and Eric A. were modest but persistent influences.

You formed a band and recorded some songs on a four-track. You sounded awful, but who cares? In those basements, in a cloud of green smoke, pounding/slapping/chunking out primate riffs while a revolving door of guest artists, a.k.a. singers, wailed to be heard over the white noise, you were the future.

You, you personally, were never popular. You were small, kind of weird, and probably, eventually definitely, gay. You were still your middle school self until you learned to slap your way around the fret board of a Fender. Then, suddenly, you had a marketable skill besides drawing comic books on notebook paper. The other aspiring primates accepted you as one of their own and there was a community of sorts. Basement/noise/purpose.

The band that formed actually had some form, at least for a couple years. You played at the school dance, along with two somewhat well-known bands from the downtown scene. Plaid shirts and stocking caps: an early nineties Pacific Northwest semi-formal in full effect.

You played the clubs downtown, all now long gone. You, personally, discovered an early aptitude for networking and talked your way into gigs with bands you met at shows. Your band, now in its "classic line-up," had about six months of not being completely unknown, at least among people who went to every show there was to see.

You played—and this is no bullshit, this is for real—one of the same clubs Nirvana did before they were Nirvana, before they were rock history. People stood and danced at your shows. OK, you weren't very good, but you still took second place at a Battle of the Bands at the local community college. That was your last show.

Some members of the band were growing apart. Some would eventually grow closer together. You were out of high school now, making a go at the above mentioned community college. The band broke up. Nobody, or mostly nobody, had time. You and the guitar player were best friends during high school, but your time spent together now was becoming less and less.

Other pursuits pulled at your attention. Tectonic plates shifted. You moved to LA. The singer and the drummer got married and made a couple babies. You're still wrapping your head around that one.

2

A good thirteen years after your heyday, you and the guitarist reconnect via, you guessed it...MySpace. Hey, this was four years ago, fuck off. You are relieved at this reunion, mostly because it gives you a chance to apologize for, quite frankly, avoiding contact. Too much time had passed; you were worried about coming out to your long-time and occasionally— back then, at least—homophobic friend. But all seems smooth, and you make plans to hang out together on your next trip back home, with him, his wife, and his three daughters.

The day comes, and you meet up at a bar. There are the awkward hellos, how-you-beens, you-look-goods. You both look like older versions of yourselves, though by all accounts you've both aged well. You are invited over for more beers and to hang out. You accept, and as the evening wears on you feel more and more like your old self.

You hang with your buddy from high school and his family, and eventually the TV and Xbox come on, and everyone is taking their positions for Rock Band. You're on bass, your friend on guitar, his wife on drums, and his oldest daughter on the mic. You work through a case of Miller High Life and the 1990s alt-rock canon. It feels pretty good.

You tell the oldest daughter that when you weren't much older than she is, you and her dad used to do this for real, sometimes in the same club Nirvana played. She rolls her eyes. You smile. It feels pretty fucking good.

For one more evening, at least, you're a rock star.

IMAGINE IF YOU...

BY GREG RUTTER

...set about a program to give an eight-year-old child all the wisdom and experiences an adult has as soon as possible. You'd put him on a very serious curriculum so that he had to take all his tests to get his high school diploma in one year. And then you'd give him a paycheck that he had to earn. Next he'd have to buy a condo. At only eight years old, he'd have done things that some grown-ups haven't done by the time they're forty.

Then he should see a dead body. Any one will do, just to remind him that mortality is a reality. After that the wheels would already be in motion. He'd get married to someone that'd be wrong for him. He'd quit the job you made him get and get another that pays more but forces him to work more hours. His thick little eight-year-old hairline would begin to recede. He'd start drinking more; first one with dinner, and then two, and then he'd have a few at lunch a couple days a week. He'd eye men's magazines jealously, staring at the lithe twenty-three-year-olds with the time to go to the gym. He'd have elaborate fantasies about how all the swimsuit models in the back of the magazine had insane orgies with the chiseled models in the fitness section.

By the time he was ten, he'd make big resolutions to change. He'd start running. He'd enter a half marathon and finish with a pretty good time. He'd lose all the weight he'd put on from drinking so much. He'd wake up and look at his body in the mirror. If you'd done your job well enough, he'd have the confidence to realize he was married to the wrong person, get a divorce, and move back into the first condo he'd bought. He'd be happier, remembering what it's like to be young again, even though he'd only be twelve at this point.

Eventually he'd meet someone else that shares his view on life a little better. She'd be active and fun. They'd get a dog together, have a private wedding with a few friends somewhere tropical like Bali, and feel happy together.

And then, one day, he'd be watching a movie. It would be stupid and pointless, something about cars that turn into tanks. There would be a short flashback to one of the character's childhood, and it'd cut right to his core. He'd think about how happy he was when he was eight, before he was a grown-up. He'd start crying, not sure exactly what he was missing, just that something wasn't the same. He'd be nostalgic for who he was, and feel like he'd wasted his whole life.

This would happen when he was fifteen, and he'd have a feeling of defeat come over him. A feeling like he'd had one chance, missed it, and now he's out of time. He'd probably work for a few more years but his heart wouldn't be in it anymore. He'd retire. He and his wife would move somewhere easy, like San Diego. After this he'd just sort of fade away. His neighbors would wave to him when they saw him watering his hydrangeas in the morning, but other than that they wouldn't pry into his life very much.

From that point until the time that he'd die, he'd be happy in the traditional sense. He'd laugh and smile more than he'd frown. All of life's responsibilities would be removed, so there would be no stress. His wife would still love him and treat him well.

But underneath it would still be a sad feeling that he'd wasted too much time and missed his chance. That's just what we're built to do. No matter how quickly we do it, we always wish we had more time.

TO ALL THE MEN I EVER LOVED

BY LUSIA STRUS

To you, Michael Herman. My first kiss. My first love. You leaned me against the side of your parents' bungalow, the comb in my back pocket scraping against the rough brick. I had on a yellow baby-doll T-shirt with a glittery rose decal that said "Touch of Class" in script handwriting. And when you leaned in I said, "No tongue." Your lips were soft, and I loved you.

And to you, Julio. My boss at Gallop Menswear at the Brickyard Mall. You were my first. You'd pick me up in your fancy sports car outside of Mother Theodore Guerin High School for young aspiring ladies, and you'd take me to the White Horse Motel where you taught me to do things that ladies don't do. I loved you, too.

And to Gary. The first guy to whom I said, "I love you." YouSaidItFirst. And then I—sitting curled up on my futon on the floor, spiral perm hanging in my face, drunk like the kind of drunk only college will allow—I said, "I love you, too." Then I dry heaved. You said, "Oh, that's beautiful, Lusia. Really beautiful." And recently? In LA? When we were all having our own little Big Chill sort of reunion? Tara asked how old I was when I had my first orgasm? I said, "Twenty-six," then turned to you across the table and said, "Sorry." You laughed. We all did. And I loved you right then too.

And to Armand DiBennedetto. Who I dated when I was twenty-six. Thank you. Thank you SO MUCH. Your name, Armand DiBennedetto, literally translated means "warrior of the blessed," and that you were. Now you're a dentist, and sometimes I think I should have never broken up with you.

And Mike. I wrote plays about you. I married you. I divorced you. Drugs ruined you. I thought you ruined me. But you didn't. You were there so I could feel the true desire to make someone happy, and the true, acute loneliness of lying next to someone who wasn't able to be. When I screamed, "What is wrong with you? You married a woman sixteen years younger who makes her own money, who has dropped two dress sizes SINCE we've been together, who LOVES to clean and has a borderline compulsive slash FERAL need to put things in her mouth! You married UP, motherfucker! And you're messing it up!" I wanted to make you feel bad. That isn't love. You taught me that, too. How strange to not know if you're alive or dead.

And to Crazy Chicago Pathological Liar Maserati guy. You were obsession, not love. But you lived in my head rent free for two years. I should have repo'd the Maserati as payment.

And to AA Leather Guy. I don't love you or anything. But you've got skills, mister, so you deserve a shout out.

And to Mr. Most Beautiful People. What to say? I'm sorry? It seemed like it should work. I really did try. You really are beautiful. *People* magazine thought so. So did I. Too much so, maybe. For me. Caused defensiveness. Caused insecurities. I felt fake. Like I was trying to act in a coffee commercial all the time. It was exhausting. Made me fake a lot of things. A LOT of things. How sad that is. How sad that you couldn't tell, and that I didn't feel like I could tell you. But I do think I deserve a dildo shaped like an Oscar. I'd accept it wearing a fabulous dress accessorized with regret.

And to you who is coming. Or not. Because I'd rather have nothing than settle for less. This is what I promise you: I will adore you like no other.

I AM DEFINITELY A GROWN-UP

BY KYLE KINANE

My name appears on my driver's license as Kyle Christian Kinane. As far as the rules of comedy are concerned, it's a perfect name. The hard "C" and the rule of threes, all right there in my dumb goddamned name. I never had a chance.

My license also lists my date of birth as 12/23/76, meaning I am legally and biologically thirty-four years old. This and a receding hairline are the only indications that I, Kyle Christian Kinane, am a grown, adult man.

On to the facts. I have five pieces of hot dog–inspired artwork hanging in my home, which is an apartment in Los Angeles I share with an angry Mexican. I routinely stop in the hallway in order to fart into his bedroom. That may be the source of his anger. That, and all my "accidental" nudity.

I am currently battling poison oak, which I contracted after falling off my bicycle. I fell off my bicycle because I didn't want to run over a snake that was in my path. It may have been a rattlesnake. I didn't get a good look, because I was busy falling into the poison oak. Yeah, it was probably a rattlesnake. This is what I do on weekday afternoons when everyone I know is at work. I ride my bike into rattlesnake-infested woods and then fall down. And I'm probably listening to REO Speedwagon or Suicidal Tendencies or some other dumb shit while I do it. On the bright side, my roommate is happy because being covered in poison oak has really put the kibosh on the "accidental" nudity. It's incredibly unsightly and ruins the humor of the effort.

I just remembered all I had to eat yesterday were hot dogs.

A while ago, I got a card from the doctor that says I can buy marijuana. I told him I needed it because I had anxiety. That was a lie but not really. I had anxiety because I was afraid I wasn't going to be able to smoke any marijuana before going to the movies that afternoon. One time I sold marijuana to a pregnant woman who worked at the same gas station as me. It was a long time ago, but I still feel bad about it. I hope the baby turned out nice.

So that's about it. That's how I live as a grown man. I, Kyle Christian Kinane, thirty-four years of age (according to government-approved documentation and medical records), am currently listening to my angry Mexican roommate have loud sex with an unsavory woman as I finish writing this essay. Hopefully he won't be as angry tomorrow, because he's going to get a big dose of "oops-dropped-my-towel" at breakfast, poison oak or not.

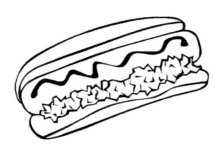

WHAT DOES IT MEAN TO BE A GROWN-UP?

DATA!

Worth of US video game industry: $10.5 million

Percentage of American households that play video games: 67

Average age of US gamer: 34

"It means not needing to be a grown-up: being able to eat dessert before dinner, do incredibly stupid things, have no onc to answer to but yourself, and live authentically."

—*TJ Olsen, 24, freelance writer, music booking agent*

"A lot of people never use their initiative because no one told them to."

—*Banksy,* Wall and Piece

STORE-BOUGHT PIE

BY MARTA RAINER

It will be one of those weeks when a cluster of old celebrities will die. The "awww" will be pushed out of you from the bellows in your chest, newly ripe for a squawk with each opening of a paper, each glance at a screen. Your "Not agains!" will sound your distaste—as if their mortal timing were spiteful, because how much are you supposed to take in a morning? You will have had to get up at all, and now this, too?

Minutes down the line, you'll have reminisced about who you were when you first enjoyed their fine achievements, and you'll have failed to unpack your melancholy. And minutes down the line, you'll have poured yourself another cup of coffee, and you will sit reading about the wars, and you will feel strangely at peace. A sad, rumbly, corporeal peace, accompanied by a teeny black and white cluster of old, dead, winged celebrities bopping about the kitchen, about three feet off the ground, like famous, haunting soap bubbles.

"It's like there's something in the water," an overly friendly, non-corporate commuter on the train will say, trapping an unfortunate woman in polite conversation—everyone else will be relieved to be overlooked by this man, and they will bury themselves behind the obituaries. Shifting and studying the seam of her purse's side carefully, the unfortunate woman will glow: *No, no, no, no, it's all too bad, but no. We don't do this, sir. This is not what we do—this chat.*

That woman radiating those thoughts will be you, you see, and that day you will be wishing that you could be doing anything, crocheting, say, instead of baldly fending people off. But you cannot do most womanly things: the cooking, the mending, the in-person nurturing. You also can't do many manly things: going toward places on horseback.

You can miss people and write unanswered letters. And you can shrug your own otherness off as "the times we live in." You can persevere. You can be that friend who still connects with others through letters—on that week of all weeks, especially.

Can it be possible, you will later wonder, *that I really am so bored, and in New York City—simultaneously?* And pasta will be put in your mouth; masticated; gone. And the dead celebrities will hover, float, weave, bump, ricochet off your notebook's page and into the bubbling bowl below. They will be laughing at you kindly: "Heaven is a delight!" they will say, and wade through the sauce.

> Dear Clint:
>
> Gosh! Guess what:
>
> A little birdie (ok, Jane Fossamer—I ran into her at the movies last week) let it slip that you and Bess are going to be PARENTS! CONGRATULATIONS to you both—that's AMAZING!
>
> And you'll be a great dad, I could always tell! In fact, if Bess wants any insight on what you'll be like as a father, tell her I can show her some tapes of the two of us in all-ll-ll-ll those high school plays where we were stuck playing the parents just because we were the tallest—your early instincts on display.
>
> Still working at the poster store—it's busy this time of year—and still painting the town red (HA HA), etc. I'm thrilled for you, and hey—if you keep me posted, I'll proudly smoke a cigar in your honor...
>
> Lots of love,
>   Benna

It will be one of those weeks when a cluster of old celebrities will die, and, lo and behold, a beloved classical flute player will fail to flout death that morning. (He will have just released a Baroque-Ambient fusion Christmas album.) Your mother will call you to gauge if you've heard. You will have. She will ask if you remember them taking you to see him play at Carnegie Hall. You will —you were eleven years old, and you'd just pitched the piano for the flute; their support was ultimately earnest. They just wanted it to stick this time, wanted you to be able to make music. And tra la la—you'll still have that nearly burnished flute in your overflowing closet. You'll put it together over the holidays and use it, with bodega holly and pine sprigs, to decorate the top of your TV.

And because you'll have no room at your place for a proper tree, you'll have been spending that week's seasonal lunch breaks lingering at street corners, removing your glove to furtively feel the needles of the imported Pittsburgh pines—stacked and taunting—or otherwise, contemplating your glove bumps, and stamping. The cold snap of your breath will hover around your head, and you'll wonder how the tree sellers can stand to be out with their ware all day.

"How do you...isn't the cold painful?"

"Eh?"

"Isn't it awfully cold?"

"Well...yeah."

"Oh." [Pause. Stamping.]

"Sure."

"Hah," you'll respond.

"Can I show you one of these?"

"Not...yet. I mean no."

"Oh."

You will collect some sample branch snippets from the bucket that he gestures to as he walks back to his hub. A friendly drunk will tell you to smile, and your leg muscles will phantom–kick kick kick him down.

You will be five minutes late to your shift today, post-lunch. You will sell 5x7 frames, 8x10 frames, an 11x17, all shiny-shiny. Also you will put aside a 4x6 display frame that apparently "just came apart" in a man's hands—you'll have to take the customer's word on this. You will sell an Ansel Adams print, a Toulouse-Lautrec, and three world-weary kittens wearing sailor hats. "Christ, these are cute," the zaftig woman heaving her way toward the counter will say. "Christ."

Dear Jess:

Thought I'd drop you a line, as no doubt you're upset about Ben Scotto, too. It's incomprehensibly sad that he's gone. Of course, I always think of YOU when I hear the Tangents on the radio...remember skipping fifth periods and driving to that sandwich shop in Port Chester (where that cute, furry guy worked), with the windows down to let in the spring air, blaring "Carmina"...speeding back for Beebe's quizzes, never prepared, but we aced them anyway, feeling like fricking rulers of the world, full on cold cuts! No one can simultaneously eat and drive like you, then or (undoubtedly) now.

And will the Pennings be visiting your parents this Christmas, or his? Well, if you'll be back in town, give a call—let's catch up properly.

Love,
Benna

The winged mini-celebrities will have messed up your bed sheets. An assorted horde will be learning Bulgarian folk dancing on the mattress by your shoulders, and it will cause problems as you'll lie there, trying to sleep. It will be one of those weeks when your rhythm will somehow be off—sleeping too much will leave you exhausted, though you won't have been able to sleep in on the one recent day that you were allowed to. You just simply won't be able to lie there anymore.

That night—bullying sleep to come and take you—you will be compelled to roll around a bit and try to smother the celebrities. Despair-displacing action. Most will take the hint and scurry down toward your feet to play Telephone. Then: hissing and giggling and gurgling at your feet. The folk-rock guitarist will deliberately screw up the phrase being passed from ear to ear. You will be infuriated. How will you be able to drift when dead celebrities insist on carrying on with their ephemeral balderdash? How will you ever get enough sleep, you'll think. "Come, they tol' me, arhhum pa pum pum..." the rap artist will croon, and not without artistry. The art historian will clap unashamedly and light a spliff.

"OUT?" a spotted lump will scoff at you on the next day, 4.7 hours into being on your feet. No one will be able to hear the green hum of the lights with all that goddamn jingle-jangling. No one will be able to hear your mind clanking like a turnstile. "How can you be OUT of Tangents posters? It's Christmas! God, what are you people THINKING? It's the perfect goddamn stuffer idea since, you know, and everyone's freaking OUT of this. Go...gahhh pluh pluh pluhhhhhhhhh..." Your phantom fingers will be pulling on her gummy extended tongue.

"But you see, MA'AM, they had fallen from the public's radar until just THIS WEEK, MA'AM—before Scotto" [you'll eat this word] "no one had much use for their merchandise for years, unless one chose to go to a collectors convention that dealt in that subject matter. OK?"

"Jesus. Fine. What the hell am I supposed to get for my sister now? Jesus."

"Well, him we've got posters of."

Ha ha, lump. Laugh at my little joke.

You'll suggest making a collage of obit photos. She will buy—to your surprise—a frame, in desperation. She will not be happy with you, and you won't smile as widely as you will for the others who do you the courtesy of not making eye contact.

Dear Jenna:

It's Benna! Merry merry Christmastime! Mine will be white, I think, while yours should be golden and sunny (this=how I desire things to be for you all once again, not just that you're in San Diego). Guess what I'm baking right now? The oatmeal cookie recipe from YOUR MOM! Nothing better, as you well know. And I'm thinking of you both as she goes into her treatments. Please send her my love and update me. I will now reiterate my yearly threat (I'm very motivated this time) to come and visit you both out there, as soon as I save up some. I just don't know where the money has gone in the past! (Must have been all that lingerie for all those hot dates, ha ha.)

I read your latest editorial online, and I was so proud. Maybe one day I'll get up the courage to send you one of my poems. Or maybe (mercifully) not.

But in all seriousness I am thinking of you constantly. You know how well I can imagine what you're going through. It can't be an easy time for you—I wish I could help. But I'm here—on the other end of the phone, if nothing else—should you need me for anything, oh ex-college-roomie extraordinaire.

So: Let's relish these holidays as best we can, my dear!

Peace and Love,
     B

It will be one of those weeks when a cluster of old celebrities will die, and you will not. You will pack an overnight bag. You will pack a small honey-glazed ham in this overnight bag—a rind of plastic separating its juice from your Christmas Eve clothes. You will venture into the suburbs by commuter rail. There you will slovenly shave carrots, gulp wine, baste meat, eat candy—all, regrettably, as a public act, documented by your brother and his new digital camera toy. You will roast things, though be shivery. When you get an inevitable sweater, you will actually be thankful for it and put it on right away. You will realize you'd forgotten to take the price off your mom's bath salts. Your snorty laugh will be made fun of, and you will find comfort in the predictability of this. You will catch some of the Pope's Vatican mass later, alone on the couch with some tea, a gift bow stuck to your pate, making solitary merry—you will toggle between this and MTV. You will listen on your own Walkman to the CDs that you brought as a gift for your brother.

"And are you jooooooooooooooooyful, Benna?" the late sitcom starlet will whisper into your ear. You will swat, then give up. She'll crawl into its curve and hang out, as if on a person-sized crescent moon that vaudeville houses once swung people from. Near the hearth, a basketball player will make a mummy out of a talk show host, mischievously wrapping him around and around with the ribbon that will come off of your dad's new...box of prunes! A joke from your mom! You'll all howl like jungle animals when he opens it. She'll be thrilled. A+ reaction, Kids! Dad and his crazy bowels, ha ha!

Your mom will be Santa Claus. "Take that, winged celebrities. Freaking eternally SANTA Claus."

You'll wonder, as you'll rub a toe, if Santa ever has cause to drop the jolly, get his ya-yas out.

Your room will not be unlike it was when you left it behind. Nearing 2am, you will be moved to flip up the weighty mattress and pull out old scrapbooks that remain stored and secret among the massive clumps of dust beneath—still historically naughty scrapbooks, though now recognizable as long-defunct evidence of stress-less kissings, love letters, and plans; piles of stupid kids with funny hair, living.

At 3am, your head will twitch at a sharp creak of the settling bedroom door. You'll be briefly convinced that a procession of this year's Top 100 Most Missed is entering your room in hushed jubilation and choir robes, to hoist you above them like determined ants and carry you away as their prize roast. You'll imagine painlessly turning on a spit, the flames tickling your long-untouched skin. You'll smile (you tasty trophy, you) and nestle in your down casing at the thought.

But a cough coming from outside your window will reveal the partial-derivation of your fantasy: your brother standing on the non-parental side of the house, sneaking a cigarette, and whisper-singing "Lo, How a Rose" to his current college sweetheart on a cell phone. Well...where the hell will he have learned that? Not from you. Not from you or yours.

Too embarrassed to eavesdrop, you will head down to interrupt him, armed against the cold with just boots and blankets over jammies—you will quickly regret not having gone for your coat, but nevertheless stubbornness and loneliness will push you directly out the back door.

Your brother will hang up almost immediately.

"Heard you," you'll say.

"Sorry," he'll say. Stamping.

"No, no. Whatever. You didn't have to."

"She had to go anyway."

"Mmmmm. So...what's she like?" You'll sort of want to know.

"She's all right. She's cool. She's in New Mexico. For the break."

"That's where her folks are?"

"Yup."

"Oh."

And you'll reach over and thumb his cigarette to take an awkward drag, not because you smoke, but because it will seem to be the best way to stay out there with him, as you won't know how to be a big sister so devoid of advice and stay otherwise. You will long for him to ask things, and you will dread his asking anything. You'll be paralyzed by the interrogative.

Stamping.

"It's weird, this year," he'll offer.

"Mom misses Grandma so much." That will be terribly true.

"It's so...weirdly..."

"Hmmm. I...I really miss the pie."

Maybe we should have gone away, you both will think.

"Where, though?" he will say.

"Don't know. Oh God, why, why am I doing this?" you will demand of his unreturned cigarette and carry on sucking it into you. You'll need to finish what you start; you'll haven't had started much in months.

Anyway he'll have lit another one.

"Disgusting," you'll say.

"Sharon's dad gave her a DVD player."

"Your girlfriend?"

"Sure."

Bouncing knees. You'll try to remember if freezing to death is one of the top worst ways to go. You'll be almost positive drowning is. As well as watching the knowledge spill out of one's own head, like a trickle from a carafe of orange juice poured into the thirsty maw of each day's new universe. Irretrievable and frustrating as all hell, and slow...slow.

"So, what...are you going to marry this girl, ha ha?"

"Probably not." he'll balk. "Naw."

It will be one of those weeks when a cluster of old celebrities will die, and so: more food for you. Some winter mornings, there is none so good as dinner for breakfast at one in the afternoon; a side of whipped cream with everything; your cold bare feet tucked under your torso; surrounded.

"Thanks for doing the dishes, Benna."

You won't have done the dishes.

Giggling and scampering. Slappings of palm on palm.

WHAT IT MEANS TO BE A GROWN-UP

A POEM

BY NEIL HAMBURGER

Debt
Desperation

DIVORCE

Bad Reviews
Cancellations

DESPAIR

Storage Lockers
Estate Sales

RUIN

Frozen Pizzas
Canned Fruit
Store Brand Vodka

FAILURE

Apathetic Motel Maids
Worn-Out Mattresses
Thin Grayish Sheets
Oily On/Off Switches
Bed Bugs

PARANOIA

Broken Phones
Burnt-Out Turn Signals
Slow-Leaking Tires Riddled With Nails
Melted Ice In Dirty Cups
Smudged Glasses And Failing Eyesight

DISAPPOINTMENT

Young And Stupid Pig People
Ghastly Music Made By And For Druggies
Vainglorious Freeloaders Espousing YouTube

INSULIN

FEET

BY KATHLEEN AKERLEY

A street, in evening, twelve hours after a bombing. Two adolescent boys are picking through debris. One grabs the other and pulls him into hiding.

PETER
Feet!

THOMAS
Where?

PETER
Where Mason's was. In the door. Nearly buried there, see?

THOMAS
Oh yeah. Not moving.

PETER

Of course not moving.

THOMAS

Maybe it's a mannequin.

PETER

In Mason's?

THOMAS

But they've already come through for bodies. They wouldn't miss those.

PETER

Maybe somebody moved her. Or she was covered before and it's gone. It's just her feet, I didn't see her right away. Maybe looters moved her, or maybe they just didn't see her feet.

Another boy runs in.

PETER

Michael! Over here.

THOMAS

Where've you been?

MICHAEL

I was over on Lombardy Court. I thought you meant the bombing there.

THOMAS

Lombardy Court was bombed three days ago, Michael. I know you know because your aunt told me about you finding her an earring.

PETER
Pussy. Where were you?

MICHAEL
I went to Lombardy Court. I forgot, OK?

THOMAS
What's in the bag, Michael?

MICHAEL
Fruit. It's a peach I think. I didn't look. My mom made me take it.

PETER
Where were you, Michael? Were you with your mommy getting fruit?

MICHAEL
Look, it's stupid, OK? The doctor got her on this kick that I take too long on the toilet, so she's making me eat fruit and she's timing it and if it's longer than a minute I have to eat more fruit and I'm not allowed to take in anything to do because she says gaming makes me even more tense already. Yeah, it's a peach.

THOMAS
Wow. That sucks. Do you at least get to pick what you eat?

PETER
Do you at least get to pick your own nose?

THOMAS/MICHAEL
Fuck you.

THOMAS
Michael, look in the door of Mason's.

MICHAEL
Feet! Ewww!

PETER
Thomas thinks it's a mannequin.

MICHAEL
In Mason's?

PETER
I say we go look.

Silence. Michael begins to eat his peach.

MICHAEL
She has nice shoes.

PETER
What, you want them? Share that.

Michael does. All the boys eat.

MICHAEL
No, I just think...well, she must have been doing something kind of important.

THOMAS
I wonder why no one's taken them.

PETER
Because they're all home with their mommies eating fruit.

THOMAS *(to Michael)*

Maybe she didn't die right away. Maybe she was underneath stuff and she crawled out right after the rescuers and the looters had gone.

MICHAEL

Maybe.

PETER

Then why are her feet pointed out? If she was crawling it'd be her hands or her head.

THOMAS

Well, either way that means there might still be some nice stuff. Maybe she was married and there's a ring.

MICHAEL

Maybe she was pretty.

PETER

OK, so let's go look. I said already.

Silence.

MICHAEL

Did Mr. Mason die?

PETER

Oh...I don't know.

THOMAS

I don't think so. We'd have heard. Wouldn't we?

MICHAEL
But wouldn't he have come by his store by now? He's had way enough time for check and release.

PETER
What's your point?

MICHAEL
It's just...weird. Don't you think there's something weird about this? That lady here and no one else?

PETER
Good. Come on.

He gets up and starts across the street. The others follow. The scene shifts to blackness—it is the interior of Mason's. Perhaps we hear the sound of a bell ringing on the back door of a business opening and closing. In darkness:

THOMAS
Don't start freaking, Michael. It hasn't been long enough for rats.

MICHAEL
Thanks.

PETER
Or banshees.

MICHAEL
Shut up.

THOMAS
Who's got matches?

MICHAEL
I think I do.

PETER
Shit! I touched her. I touched her face.

THOMAS
Shhhh!

Michael fumbles with his matches and gets one lit. Lying at Peter's feet is a nicely dressed woman's body with a watermelon where the head should be.

THOMAS
What the...what face? You said you touched her face. That's a watermelon.

MICHAEL
She lost her head in the explosion. But there's no blood.

THOMAS
And no head.

PETER
I did touch her face. Her mouth was wet, and her nose was pointy.

The match goes out, burning Michael who yelps and has a harder time lighting the next one. When it gets lit her head is a festive wad of gold aluminum foil. The boys stare at it until the match goes out. Silence.

PETER
Light another one.

THOMAS
Don't.

PETER
Do it.

Michael lights a third match. Where her head should be there is a huge spider. The match goes out in the subsequent frenzy, perhaps the sound of young feet clambering on rubble. Silence. In darkness:

MICHAEL
I just shit myself and it took way less than a minute.

THOMAS
That's good.

Silence.

PETER
Light another one.

MICHAEL
There aren't any more.

PETER
Liar. Pussy liar. Don't you want to see what's next?

Pause. Michael lights a fourth match. There is no object but a hole in the debris/floor where the head should be. A hand is beckoning from inside the hole. Silence. The match goes out. In darkness:

PETER

You go first.

END OF PLAY

THE HIDDEN BEAUTY OF ANONYMOUS SURVIVAL

BY GENEVRA GALLO-BAYIATES

When I was in college in my early 20s, I used to walk through the streets of Boston at night, through the tree-lined neighborhoods on crooked sidestreets, and peer into the lit windows of every house.

Scenes of normalcy, of quiet, simple evenings. People eating dinner. People watching TV. Talking or cooking or drinking or dancing in quiet summer evenings with the sun steadily dropping behind the city skyline.

I remember feeling a sense of longing. Like I was peeking into a Norman Rockwell painting and vicariously enjoying the warm serenity of a stability absent in my childhood. Knowing full well it was stolen contentment.

And then I moved to Chicago.

And I still peered through windows on dark winter evenings, but this time it was different.

As I approached my 30s, I began to ridicule what I thought was lifeless consistency and unchallenging routine. These lives were boring.

Predictable. Repetitive.

The gray-cloaked, dead-hearted, empty-eyed endpoint known as "growing up" or "becoming an adult."

Committed lives equated with frozen aspirations and an avalanche of compromise until nothing was left but a pretty, empty picture in a four-square prison.

But now I'm approaching my 40s. And I still walk down the streets in my Evanston neighborhood, returning from the park with my husband and daughter as we search for a cat named Lily we met last summer...

...and there are lawnmowers and the sound of kids riding bikes fast down hills —racing to avoid predatory bedtimes. The clinking of glass and soft strains of music, fireplace aromas and desperate grilling in the fleeting autumn.

And it all seems so beautiful. The routine hum of normalcy despite the inevitable stress of life. The incredible strength and determination it takes to get dinner on the table, to spend time together as a family, to remember to say please and thank you and smile at each other and talk about your day.

That doesn't sound so hard.

But it is. In a really good way.

WHAT DOES IT MEAN TO BE A GROWN-UP?

DATA!

Average age of *People*'s Most Beautiful (female):

36

Average age of *People*'s Sexiest Alive (male):

37.5

"Maybe it's me, but I feel like the more I learn, the more hopeless and small I feel, and I wonder how I can really effect change. But I'm going to try, and fail, and act, and express, and do everything that I can to just be."

—*Nicole, 23, worried all the time*

"You've made a life where no one tells you what to do. Now the only tyrant that you're working for is you. It's never easy to keep all the promises you make. No one's gonna get you fired if you just give yourself a break."

—*Craig Carothers, "Little Hercules"*

BECAUSE

WE'RE WORKING WITHOUT A NET HERE, PEOPLE

BY JACQUELYN LANDGRAF

In 2003 she was in Dublin walking home from rehearsal with her friend. She was biting into an apple when her friend stepped forward directly in front of a speeding bus, forgetting that traffic came from the right. The apple was wholly in her mouth when she sprang forward and tackled her friend back to the curb, an instant before she became Irish roadkill. The friend was hysterical; she cried, too. But now she thinks about how easily she could have choked on that apple...the apple of heroism.

She's been a bit wary of scarves ever since she first heard about Isadora Duncan. The car turns the corner, fabric catches in the wheel, neck snaps in two, and so much for modern dancing and flapper parties and Italian lovers. Death by accessories, she thinks, and refuses to ride her bike.

There was a brief period in high school when she would black out in the shower. During this same time she would quite often fall all the way down the sixteen stairs from her bedroom to the first floor of the house. This phase was never explained: anemia and cancer and vertigo ruled out. So she thought perhaps she was acquiring superpowers, or maybe entering a higher state of being, and accepted it as a given. But now sometimes she looks down the stairs to the subway and feels terrified.

She's not sure why now the fear of instantaneous death creeps more and more into her daily life. As she waits for the train, packs into the elevator, turns the light out for the night: perhaps tonight will come the fire? Or the rapist-slasher? Another tornado in Sunset Park? She wonders how long it would take for her loved ones to know she was gone. She lives alone. If she died on a Thursday, her students wouldn't register her absence 'til Monday.

Maybe it's because she doesn't have health insurance, yet she does have life insurance. Maybe it's because it used to be easy to picture heaven and hell, but now she's not at all sure. Maybe she's afraid to get old, but what's the alternative? She sure doesn't want to go. Especially now. She's so full of promise, don't you agree? And full of vivacity? And interesting looking?

She knows that when her time comes, she's not gonna have much say in the matter. So she's not living life in fear. But she is saving her breath. Because if that last gasp comes too fast, she'll take another one please.

The author asks of you two things as you read this story. 1) Please imagine that there is a very loud, almost mythic gong next to you. And a big imaginary mallet for the gong. You will be called upon to sound this imaginary gong for the duration of this story, but please feel free to keep it next to you for as long as you wish, perhaps for your entire life, because the author has found that secretly beating on imaginary gongs can sometimes make ordinary events feel much more profound. 2) Please note what time it is right now.

Sound the imaginary gong!

Sound the imaginary gong!

Sound the imaginary gong!

Sound the imaginary gong!

Sound the imaginary gong! And again! And again!

Please note what time it is now. It is probably about two minutes since the last time you looked, depending on how fast a reader you are. Turn the clock back to the time it was when you began. This never happened...

ONE AFTERNOON

BY JEFFREY CRANOR

One afternoon, he arrived home only to find he was already there. It took a moment, but he did understand that it was himself he was talking to. The two hes laughed at the brief confusion and subsequent mutual realization. Later they laughed less.

The other he—he-two, we'll call him, since he only just now appeared in he-one's apartment—moved comfortably, familiarly around the other's home, eating snacks from the pantry and completely understanding all of the electronics.

The intrusion by his doppelgänger initially intrigued he-one, but it soon evolved into fright and then hesitant trust. And after a brief adjustment and some planning, they found a new rhythm to their lives, or just "their life," as they called it.

The hes, of course, alternated workdays. This was fine by the boss and most co-workers, as long as the hes briefed each other and stayed on top of duties. Some co-workers wished that they, too, could have second selves.

He-one and he-two watched a lot of movies together. They almost always agreed on what they liked in a movie. But some nights he-two would want to watch, say, a suspense thriller, while he-one would want, say, an even-tempered foreign classic.

Mostly their life was smooth.

They did lose their girlfriend, though. The relationship between the two hes and her had become suddenly intense with sexual and existential complexities. "Fuck this," the girlfriend might have callously uttered upon bidding the two—who as a boyfriend summed up to significantly less than one—farewell.

Five years later, he-two got cancer. It was detected early. A quick surgery and a few life changes placed him back into the world again. He-one's tests were negative. He-one was still, and always, healthy.

Soon after, dinners became different. The hes shared a new gym membership. Political conversations became strange, strained. He-two had a sterner brow and darker teeth now. He got a new job in an unrelated field. He wore ties more and started dating different women than he-one. He-two asked he-one for more space, some more time alone in the apartment.

"But it's my apartment," he-one retorted. "I was here first." He wasn't sure anymore, though, who was there first. They fought. They fought all the time. He-one usually apologized and they would make up. More and more, they did not make up.

One afternoon, he arrived home only to find that he was the only thing, the only one, there. It took a moment but he did understand that everything was gone. He had no furniture, no clothes, no pictures. Just blank walls, empty floors.

He moved uncomfortably, familiarly around the home, looking for the snacks and electronics.

The emptiness initially intrigued him, but it soon evolved into fright and then resignation. And after a brief adjustment, he found a new rhythm to his life.

He took off a few extra workdays. This was fine by the boss and most co-workers, as they understood that this was a rough stretch of his life. Some co-workers wished that they, too, could have all of their belongings disappear in a moment.

He watched a lot of movies. He didn't really care what movies.

Mostly his life was empty.

He did not have a girlfriend. "Relationships have intense sexual and existential complexities," he might have callously uttered, if he had someone to talk to.

Five years later, he thought he had cancer. His tests were negative. He didn't have cancer. He didn't have anything.

Soon after, dinners became different. He avoided the gym. Political conversations were non-existent. He had a plain brow and invisible teeth. He stayed in his job where he didn't have to wear ties or date women. He wanted less space, less time alone in the apartment, more things.

"It's just not my apartment," he told himself. "Without things." He wasn't sure anymore, though, what things he wanted. More and more, though, he got some things.

One afternoon, he arrived home only to find that all of the things he had were there. It took no time to understand that he had been there that morning. No one had been there since. The things that were there when he left were there when he returned. Nothing had moved or changed. He did not laugh or come to any realization about inertia.

He watched movies.

Mostly the movie characters' lives were smooth.

One afternoon, he arrived home only to find that it was night.

One afternoon, he arrived home only to arrive home.

One afternoon, he arrived home only to...

(Nevermind.)

One afternoon, he arrived home only to find that nothing was there. It took a moment but he did understand that nothing had ever been there nor would ever be there. There was no furniture, no clothes, no pictures, no door, no walls, no floor, no sky, no earth, no light, no dark. He couldn't even see himself.

One afternoon, he arrived home only to find a crowd of people holding lights and recording equipment. It took a moment but he did understand that there were questions to answer.

One afternoon, he arrived home only to leave again.

One afternoon, he arrived home to the memory of smells. The memory of food. To a hint of

Onion.

Peanut oil.

Rye bread.

And zest and greens. Cakes cooling. A refrigerator full, like a wealthy belly, the cold hum of comfort and bodily wisdom.

There was a young girl. Someone's daughter, of course, who ate only white bread and beans and smelled like tap water.

She—we'll call her that, because she was a girl—and the man never really knew each other, were never the same age, were never more connected.

Mostly her life was nothing. Except on those nights.

Special nights.

When uncles

strangers

cousins

Some man.

Yes. In this case, yes.

Some man came to visit her and her parent and her home. A special night. She, standing in the yard, arms around a stale but friendly dog with a forgettable name.

He, the man (not the dog), was not there to see her, but his being there filled her with meaning, food, comfort, care, dinner, a celebration, a reason... however fleeting. He was unaware of the impact he made.

She wore jean shorts and maybe a bow.

A chain link fence.

Not much grass. But wind. A breeze carrying the aromatic promise of this special night. This special guest. He was unaware that he was special. He was unaware of many things.

She breathed in. More wind. She breathed back against it. The food. The smell. I mean...

(I mean, the flavor, really.)

The taste, filling the belly, the body, the soul, the heart, the absence of time, and the dissipation of age.

Manchego. An orange. Cardamom. And oatmeal. Or hot tea steam. A honeysweethoneylovingsweethoneyroll that perfectly conformed to the shape of her mouth and...

(You don't know nobody. You don't owe nobody nothing. That time when that bad thing happened in that school by that friend who betrayed that ideal. That doesn't exist for now. You don't have that anymore, in this this. This time.)

In a swallow. Dissolved. Honeysweethoneystickystickyhoneysweet.

A hot goodbye on a warm hello of calm

               of peace

                     a piece of tasty steak or wine and no regrets

She breathed.

...

The wind did not breathe, only blew. No regrets.

A pause. (Count to 50.) Some. Some regrets.

Soon after, he, the man, left. For she, dinners became different. The same. No smells. No man. No special nights. She threw viscous objects past the dog. The dog followed and returned them. The road between the wires of the fence stayed a road, completely understanding inertia. She wore holes in her old jeans, which later became new shorts.

She didn't want anything. She didn't know how to want.

One afternoon, he arrived home only to find a stone shaped like an animal he had never heard of.

One afternoon, he arrived home only to find that he was arriving home behind himself.

One afternoon, he arrived home only to find that he was the only one there. It took most of his life, but he did understand that this was not unusual, as he did, after all, live alone. He laughed at the brief confusion and subsequent realization. Later he laughed less.

He—we'll call him just that, he, since he was the only he in his apartment—moved comfortably, familiarly around his own home, eating snacks from his pantry and completely understanding all of his electronics.

He worked every day he was supposed to work. This was fine by the boss and most co-workers, as long as he stayed on top of his duties. Some co-workers wished that they, too, could stay on top of their duties.

He watched a lot of movies. Some nights he would want to watch, say, a suspense thriller, while some nights he would want, say, an even-tempered foreign classic.

Mostly his life was smooth.

Five years later, he got cancer. It was detected early. A quick surgery and a few life changes placed him back into the world again.

Soon after, dinners became different. He got a new gym membership. He had a plainer brow and impotent teeth now. He got a new job in an unrelated field. He wore ties more and dated different women. He started to want more time to himself. More time alone in his apartment.

He never smelled things, only remembered what things smelled like.

One afternoon, he arrived home only to find himself, figuratively speaking.

One afternoon, he arrived home.

One afternoon, he did not. But then, later, he did.

A FOUND-ITEM LOOK AT
WHAT IT MEANS TO BE A GROWN-UP
FROM OUR FRIENDS AT

FOUNDMAGAZINE.COM

BANK
XXX LARGE T-SHIRTS
KNOX GELATIA
BREATH ASSURES
SHAVING CREAM
DEP GEL
NORE SOAP
STRING

7. Buy gifts
- Anniversary
- Birthday
- Fathersday
- Amy Amstuz

8. Go to the outt
- buy

Anti Diarrheal
(modim A D)

Equate Monoxidell
(Rogain)

59

Feed Animals

Sundays Objecti...

- Clear up Co...
- Go see if ...
  truck
- Trisha Ma...
- Personal

Flowers
Pads
alcohol swa...

TSP...
TOOTHPASTE
BRUSHES
KITCHEN TOOLS - Bill
B.O.Calde PATTI PA
GARBAGE BAGS
FILE for Receipts

I will not...
swalow my tounge
choke on my spit
bite anyone
hit anyone unless
they atack me
Throw UP
cry in public
throw things at
people
throw things when I
am mad
lose my temper
run in circles
screaming
hit people over the
head with anything
atempt to kill a
prophesor
Deck a prophesor into
the reserch computers

comit murder

chef hat
Eye patch
Mustache
clapboard
headsets
posterboard
juice
spiders

ski pants
Don't
Books

Don't forget SKI SUIT

WHAT DOES IT MEAN TO BE A GROWN-UP?

"Out of your strength
you make a distance. Then you
see,

and start to cross. You think
of what you want to say,
and you forget, deliberately.
Go back to the beginning. Think
about it.
Take, if you like, all day."

—Tony Hoagland, "Poem for Men Only"

"…she has only this self, the
one she is, and it seems to
believe itself to be
overriding and final but is
merely a memory of
someone her future self
once knew."

—Deb Olin Unferth, "Once She Was"

DATA!

Percentage of women 25–34 in
United States living with
parents:

8 in 2009

10 in 2011

"It means that you are no
longer terrified to take tests
because you are fully aware
that they are beyond
importance. I'm still
waiting."

—C. Z. Hansen, 52,
education advocate

A PARTIAL ENCYCLOPEDIA OF AGES 17–25

BY JOSEPH FINK

Memories of movement, of misunderstanding

Mérida, Mexico. I am waiting for a bus on a corner I do not know in a country that is not mine. Walk me blindfolded half a mile and I'll be lost forever.

Everything is pastel. The sky is a hot sheet of glass during the day, and even at night the air is thick and hot. Sleeping feels like drowning, so I am always tired.

The bus I am waiting for comes. I get on and wait for El Centro, downtown. It should only be a fifteen-minute ride. Forty minutes later, I am worried. The bus has been crowded and not crowded, people pushing in and rushing out, like a nervous heartbeat.

I got on the bus going the wrong direction, that is what has happened.

I don't know how long the bus route is. The bus is empty, and we are passing though neighborhoods of half-finished houses and gated factories. The driver looks back at me in his mirror and asks where am I going? and I tell him and he grunts. We circle the city in silence together for an hour and a half, riding the slow orbit back to where I belong.

Memories of transformation, of ruins, of love, of moments that are more important than they seem

California, then Cambodia. The first time I saw the Angkor Wat, I was ten years old, sitting cross-legged on a couch near my father's grand piano, reading a *National Geographic*. I was shy, and do-well-in-school, and spent most of my time reading. The jungle temple in the magazine was impossible.

Ten years later, I am there. My hand slips around Jenny's waist, and I feel wet shirt, then slick skin, then rough denim. Above us there is the shadow of a tower, then pale blue light, then shadow, then light, and then shadow. Her face is eyes, then nose, then lip, then tongue, then lip, and then chin. My life is transformation, then stability, and then transformation. We are exactly the sum of our parts.

She takes a picture of me in front of the Wat. I look at her and I love her, and so from the photo I smile at the world, loving every person who looks back at me through it. I am caught in a moment in which I am already the result of what I have been, and not yet the cause of what I will be next.

Memories of eating, of creation, of moments that are exactly as important as they seem

Topanga, California. My sister gets married on a hillside where the light is more color than light. I sit in a folding chair. And now we are both adults.

It's only been two months, but what are we supposed to do? Halt our family forever in honor of our dead?

Yes, I suppose that is a possibility. But here we are, folding chairs and a breeze and the sunset, right on cue. There are vows and the other business of lifelong commitment, and we blow bubbles instead of throwing rice.

Two months before now we had gathered around our father in his hospital room, which had a beautiful view of the Hollywood Hills that he couldn't see from the bed. Three months from now my sister would be pregnant, and she would call to tell me, and then interrupt telling me to shout to her husband that he has taken the wrong freeway, and now they are going the wrong way.

It is dizzying, the ordinary business of life.

The catering for the wedding is done by an Indian restaurant, served in foil trays, and it's good. We spell out the new couple's last name in Christmas lights on the window. The bathrooms are simple, and clean. I remember a bucket in the corner, with a green sponge. There's dust on my shoe. I pee. I eat.

That is it. That is how we change forever.

Memories of ruins, of rain, of smells I did not like, of people I will never see again but am Facebook friends with

Rome, summer. Sandra is the only one there when I arrive, but she does not speak English, so I wield my clumsy Spanish to make conversation. She produces a long, thin cigarette, a brand from Spain, and lights it. It smells terrible. The scent watches over us as I apologize for not knowing how to say whatever it is I would like to say at that moment, and as she forgives me.

Summer rain begins to fall, chasing us all to cover. The other friends aren't coming, we decide. She is wearing leather high-heeled shoes and they slip into the gaps between the stones. She lights another cigarette. We pass the time watching a curved bit of stone, an ancient step, or an alter, fill up with rain, spill over the edge, and fill up again.

Memories of waking, of coffee, of people I have not seen in too long but will see again

Again in Rome. I wake up and Jsa is sitting cross-legged at the window, letting the ash from her cigarette fall into an ashtray shaped like a turtle.

Good morning she says. And how were you sleeping last night?

Better than usual.

Yes, you were not making as much noise as I thought you would.

She fakes a snore and the smoke is ejected violently from her nostrils.

There is something about this room that strikes me, only I cannot place what it is. She is wearing loose black pajamas. I came back to Rome mostly to visit her. The decorations are what strike me, or the sheets on the bed, or the bookshelf. And I am still not sure what they strike me of.

I am making some coffee she says, and walks into the kitchen. I follow her.

She is German by blood, Swiss by birth. Her face is cat-like and brittle. For two years, as a teenager, she lived on the streets in Paris. All she will tell me about that time is that she took so many drugs she should not be alive. Her grandfather was a German communist, forced into the Nazi army on pain of his wife and children's death. He was eventually killed by an American soldier, and her grandmother died soon afterward. She tells me that Germans don't raise their right arms now.

She goes onto her toes and pulls a box of instant coffee down from the shelf with her left hand. I don't know what it is about this, or anything that follows. There is real ground coffee on the counter, but she stirs several spoonfuls of instant into cups of hot water.

You use twice the amount they say, and it is like espresso she tells me. I take a sip from my cup, which is glass and decorated with characters from SpongeBob SquarePants. It tastes fine.

We drink the coffee silently. I think about the people in my life who will give me a place to sleep at night, who will make me coffee in the morning. I am unclear what anything means, and I do not have any answers.

Memories of moments that are more important than they seem, of love, of intoxication, of horses, of 7th Avenue and 16th Street

New York. Meg and I meet in a small room. There are words and actions that night, and gestures. These all mean something, convey other things, add up to something else.

Later, we get drunk in a medium-sized room that I'm renting. Her plan is first the alcohol, and then we'd sleep together, and then we'd repeat, on other nights, perhaps in other rooms. We drink with my middle-aged gay roommate, an unemployed fashion photographer, and at a certain point I lie back with my arms flung over my face and say I'm very intoxicated. I say it over and over. I use that word, intoxicated, as an anchor to keep from spinning out of Earth's orbit.

Other things happen. Possibly a concert. Certainly there is a graffitied bathroom and then a drunken walk home. We come across police horses and touch their noses. She stops me, across the street from my apartment.

I'm going to ruin this corner for you.

She takes my hand.

I *like* like you.

The first thing I say is I kiss her. That says most of it. Then I say:

I'm not a good person to like.

But as it turns out, I am.

Memories of forgetting, of transformation, of boredom, of toothbrushes, of restaurants

Camarillo, CA. Make up your mind Jenny says to me. We're lying in her bed. It's too hot with the covers on, and too cold with the covers off, and the walls are white and empty, which makes the room seem smaller. Everything in the room smells like her, and I want very much to go outside.

We do some sightseeing in London. The hostel room has a mattress on the floor and a sink in the corner, and everything, the mattress, the sink, the walls, is white again. We are arguing while I try to get my toothbrush to balance on a windowsill. The windowsill is caked with dust. It's disgusting. I wipe the dust off with my sleeve. Better. I don't remember what the argument's about. I only remember the toothbrush.

We go for a trip up the California coast over a long weekend. We fight because I forgot to fill up the tank. Then we walk through a tide pool. Then we stand over a beach full of elephant seals. Then we sit together in a booth in a Mexican place. Then she's lying in the other bed and telling me that this is my revenge, that my indecision about the two of us is a tool I use to torture her. Then we are sitting in a Marie Callender's off the 101 in Pismo Beach and she asks me have you made up your mind and I say yes and she turns to the waitress and says OK, we're ready to order now.

Memories of rain, of misunderstanding, of boredom

Mérida again. I am staying at a friend's house, and have woken late, well after he has left for work. It rains, and the street outside becomes wet, then very wet, and then a flood. Soon the first tentative waves are brushing against the front door.

It stops raining, but the water doesn't lower. I wait inside for hours, watching through the window as the water settles around parked cars, and worrying about missing my flight tomorrow if the flood lasts another day.

Eventually, sick of feeling helpless, I tie plastic bags around my shoes and wade out into the filthy water, cutting a neat line through the film of oil on its surface. I reach the street to find that the house is built lower than its neighbors, and that all the water from blocks around has drained to this yard. I stand thigh deep in the huge puddle, watching cars drive on the dry street a block away.

Memories of water, of breasts, of nights, of moments that are not important at all

Tel Aviv. It's the trip's free night, and I am on an empty beach with a few people: Dan, who is one of the tour leaders; a hippie girl who has renamed herself Adventure; her friend Helen; Melissa, who edits BDSM porn in San Francisco; and Benjamin, an athletic British man who lied about being Jewish to get a free trip. We all take our clothes off and go into the water.

In warm water, naked is what you are supposed to be. I forget the complicated and awful history of this place, and the complicated and awful history of my own life, some of which hasn't happened yet, and which is, ultimately, no worse than anyone else's complicated and awful history.

The water is a wombvoid. There's no distinction between the night air, the water in the ocean, and the water inside my body. It could be that I am floating upward, gently and easily, until the air gets thin and cold and I shiver my way out of this world. Or I could be floating downward, until the water within meets the water without, and I finally get some rest.

But there are also the lights of Tel Aviv in the distance, like the idea of a city that hasn't happened yet, and there are bare tits around me, which are enjoyable in their own way.

That life could have lights and buildings and occupation and war, but also floating naked in a warm ocean, surrounded by naked women and the hushed purr of waves pushing us farther away from everything that is. It means something. Or doesn't it?

Memories that can't be shared

Hollywood. I tried to write about it and it hurt so much that after a couple sentences I actually made a sound, like I had just been cut quite badly, or burned.

Memories of eating, of not eating, of fear, of fires that never happened

Phnom Penh, Cambodia. Jenny and I are in a Tex-Mex bar about a five-minute walk from the banks of the Tonle Sap River. We're playing pool as we wait for our food to arrive. The velvet is worn, but we are terrible so it doesn't matter. The balls click and roll, ricocheting at impossible angles to avoid falling into a single pocket.

Earlier we were stranded on a riverbank along with two hundred people who were not stranded. Between us and our hotel was a highway in which there was never a pause, no space between vehicles, a wave that never broke. The locals walked back and forth across the road easily, but Jenny and I were trapped. Eventually we attached ourselves to a Cambodian man crossing the street. Cars and motorbikes barreled at us. One came so close that I felt the passenger's leg brush my own. Then we were on the other side, and the Cambodian man was laughing at us. Thank you we said. Thank you.

Earlier we were in the hotel, in the dark, both of us awake separately, separately thinking of the narrow stairway down the hall and down the tall building, no fire escapes, no other way down. I think I smell smoke, she said. We both sat up stiffly in the wet darkness, listening intently. The bathroom was hotter than the bedroom, like a cinder-block oven with a toilet. She laid her hand loosely on my thigh.

Earlier we were somewhere in between, on the highway from Siem Reap to Phnom

Penh. Our driver stopped at a roadside restaurant. We sat at the table, not eating, but watching him eat. I tried to say something, and he smiled and said he did not speak English. The plate was spotless. The water glass was sunhot. The three of us sat there, somewhere in between, eating and not eating and smiling.

And now our basket of buffalo wings arrives, so we let the ailing game die in peace and sit down to eat. The chicken is OK. Outside the crowds surge down unfamiliar streets. Outside we are frightened by our inexperience. Inside we are eating wings in a room lit pink and loud with American music.

Memories of movement, of forgetting, of repetition, of snow

We drive to Boston from New York. This is not a story. Connecticut is mostly billboards for porn shops and strip clubs. We're going for New Year's Eve, and it is snowing hard. That night, the bar does its last call at 11:30.

I remember citysnow outside, and how it changes the parking lot completely. Where I grew up, things didn't change. They only began and ended, and in between we were warm.

Meg and I fall asleep in a hotel bed with her college friend, Marcy. I wake up in early morning darkness because the TV is on quite loud. A man on TV is shouting at me in Spanish, and I feel suddenly certain the hotel will collapse. I am awake for an hour, sweating, and waiting. The hotel does not collapse.

That's not a story. I don't know how to make this a story.

On the way back we stop at a diner in Small Town Somewhere, Massachusetts. The houses and the New England fall makes me think of the movie *Halloween*. But later I rewatch it and realize that *Halloween* was filmed in Southern California, in the spring. I had been remembering it wrong.

That doesn't line up. We were there for New Year's, so how could it be fall? There were two different trips, about a year apart. I'm remembering them both simultaneously. I'm averaging them out in my head. I wonder if, given enough time, everything in my life will average out. If, when I'm older, the past will all have seemed to have happened at once.

That is, if not a story, at least an idea.

Memories of walking, of smells I did not like, of cold

Seoul, South Korea. My first time in Asia, but, more importantly, my first time in citysnow. A thirteen-hour layover, so Jenny and I are taking a short walk around the neighborhood. The air is frozen and pungent, like it's piped in from the seafood display at a supermarket.

A few hours of us walking in the snow together, in Seoul, together, for a few hours. What is there to say about moments like this except that I bought a warm red bean roll from a bakery next to a Domino's?

Memories of intoxication, of nights, of people I will never see again, of comic strips

Florence, summer. I am sitting beneath an enormous equestrian statue with a Canadian I met three hours before in the common room of the hostel. We are drink drank drunk now, two bottles of wine later. Neither of us bother with cups; we walk around Florence passing the bottle back and forth.

Today is some festival or another, and the streets are filled with people. We go down to a dark sand spit cutting out into the River Arno so we can look back at the crowds in the streets where we had just been. There is hardly any sound, only the shifting of sand beneath our feet and the quiet growl of the water, invisible in the darkness. Then suddenly we are back in those crowds, on those streets. It is blurry and wobbling, the memory. All the transitions were destroyed and I only have these isolated frames.

There is a church, but not a church. It is no longer a church. It is post-church, now some kind of avant-garde performance art exhibition hall. We follow the lines of people up the steps who are all themselves following other people, a drunken conga line through the door.

Hawaiian music, all slide guitar and exotica, roars from speakers invisible in the darkness. Where the altar had been is now an enormous picture of a nude pregnant woman, lit from behind and pulsating. There is a small wooden cubicle enclosed with curtains, and everyone is filing through it. Inside, the cubicle is lit by fluorescents, and tacked to the walls are hundreds of photocopied comic strips, an Italian clone of *Cathy*.

He passes me the bottle and I finish it off so we crack open the next. The nude pregnant woman on the altar glows brighter. Above, barely there in the dark, a painting of an angel stretches out its arms in blessing. The next morning I will wake up to such a hangover, and light will be poisonous. But right now it dances between us, and the cubicle full of comic strips, and the photo of the woman, and the angel above us, and the bottle of wine in my hands.

Memories of movement, of islands, of phone calls, of love

New York. On lunch breaks, I walk through Manhattan. Usually I head east, away from crowded Midtown, then either north past the UN or south to the East Village, before looping back to where I started.

It was difficult leaving behind my family and a father struggling with medical problems, so I call him nearly every time I take that walk. We talk for an hour every day for the three years before he dies.

And so my memory of the last years of my father, still young by any standard, still planning for a future that will never come, is a voice in mid-afternoon Manhattan, floating on waves of heat or treetop slushfall. The city speaks with my father's voice. Space as father. Time as father. Transit as father.

There are people who never have this relationship with their parents. People who remember their father as a bitter tone of voice or a threatening gesture. There are people who see me as lucky for carrying a loving father through the city in the palm of my hand. But I want more. I want those hours to come back, to last longer, to keep going. I want to touch my finger to his name in my phone and have my father reach out from some impossible place to answer.

What do I do about your death? I would say, on a Manhattan afternoon, wandering first east and then north or else south. And I would wait for the city to tell me.

Memories of movement, of forgetting, of sweatshirts

I'm on a plane. I was nearly asleep but now I am awake because of the turbulence, and the person who kicked my leg as they walked by, and worry about the things I have to do once I have landed, whatever those things are. My shoes are off and my sweatshirt is on.

My gut becomes aware of the plane's forward movement. The feeling has been there this entire time, but I only now notice it. I realize that I am so adjusted to the feeling that I cannot remember exactly what it feels like to move sideways or backward or even to sit completely still. The curved plastic ceiling looks like a wave, and the overhead compartments look like land the wave is breaking against.

Beneath the waves and the land is a tiny window of sky. Everyone in the plane, all of us, are facing forward and moving forward, and we can't remember what it feels like to do anything else.

Memories of vacations, of love, of smells that I liked, of water

Point Reyes Station, California. It is a vacation with Meg and my family, the last one we will take with my father. I would like, very much, to pinpoint a specific moment, some telling detail, that would explain why this vacation was so important.

There was the frog that lived in the pond in front of the rental home, and who was invisible except when he chose to pose on the rocks, like a proudly nude sunbather. The vacationing with Meg went smoothly, which is the real test of a relationship. There was the smell of herbs and salt whenever I stepped outside, and at night the air was thick and cool.

I can't find it, the one that will explain. My parents came to Point Reyes when they were in college, before they were married. They hiked there, through a tunnel of trees leading to an ocean view. They were younger than me then. That, of course, is impossible.

All through my childhood, we went to Point Reyes yearly to camp, and to hike that trail. It is a beautiful trail in a beautiful place, and nothing more. But it is also the passageway I imagine we walk when we are born, and again when we die. I imagine that, as our eyes close for the last time, we find ourselves at the trailhead. We stop, briefly, in the big meadow halfway with benches carved out of whole logs. And then we continue, on a trail rising and falling, to a view of an ocean, an ocean more vast than we had imagined, exactly as vast as we had hoped.

Memories of confusion, of movement, of phone calls, of places I never thought I'd be, of walking

Brooklyn. I arrive with two suitcases and an address on a bit of paper. I don't know where the address is, I don't know anyone in New York City, and I don't know whether this, or anything else I have ever done, is the right thing to do.

The taxi driver looks at the address for a long time and then asks me where it is. I shrug. He sighs, and starts driving under the principle that if we drive through enough of the city, we'll eventually, statistically, have to pass my destination. And, eventually, we do. The apartment is on a tree-lined street in Brooklyn. The door's locked, and I have no key. I call one of my soon-to-be roommates, who tells me that he'll be home in a few hours, and to sit tight. And so I sit, on the steps next to the trash can.

Later the roommate will arrive to let me in, and I'll drop off the suitcases and walk several miles to buy a bed. The bed can't be delivered until the next day, and so I'll sleep on the floor for a night. As weeks and months and years pass, I'll get more furniture, and then move, and then move again. My girlfriend back home will no longer be my girlfriend, and then she'll be engaged to someone else. I'll meet someone else too, and then we'll have been together for years. My father will die. My hometown will become somewhere I just visit. I'll know exactly where each of my apartments are. And, just days before writing this, I'll sit up in the middle of the night, look around a room full of things I own, and say out loud to no one What am I doing here? And where's my father?

But first, I wait with my suitcases on some stairs, on a tree-lined street, in Brooklyn, in a lifetime which will contain a lot of waiting, and a lot of other things too.

Memories of intoxication, of living rooms that belong to other people

Galway, Ireland. We are all, the gay man, and the woman I was with, and many others, in someone's apartment, high and drunk, and watching a priest talk on the God Channel. The woman is making out with someone else. Was he there before? Where did he come from?

Later, other events. The trip ends, and I come home, and, then, I leave again.

Memories of people I hope to see again, of phone calls, of _____, of video games

Camarillo, California. I am on the phone with my best friend and I am telling him that I know _____ and that it's ok, and he is telling me that ____ not _____, and then we never speak again.

Once, we had been inseparable. We made murder mysteries with an old video camera and played hours upon hours of video games. Now our separation seems easy and unsurprising. I find myself looking at this friendship as though it were an object, a block of wood, say, trying to see how it has changed. What has cracked, or what is missing. But all I see are two people, doing and saying nothing, quietly letting their friendship dissipate.

It isn't as simple or clean as I am trying to make it sound. He had said some horrible things about me behind my back to mutual friends, and I only had known _____ (I had long suspected) because of snooping that I knew was stupid, and was, these years later it has become apparent, unforgivable for him.

We had been friends for eight years, and, as of this writing, we haven't spoken for six. We both moved from California to New York, and now live maybe a half hour apart. Occasionally it feels as though we're still in that breath after I said I know _____, the soft drone of the line in our ears, waiting for something, anything, else to happen.

He has a girlfriend now, I hear. I don't know if he still goes to church. I hope, above all else, that he is happy.

Memories of phone calls, of art, of love, of sun, of fountains

Brooklyn. I call Jsa in front of an audience as part of a performance art workshop, and I get her voicemail. I leave a message saying I'll call back the next day, and then I never call her again.

I can't explain why I don't. Certainly it's not entirely my fault. Her replies to previous emails and texts were sporadic, and she has refused to join any website that might allow her to keep in touch easily. But still, the fact remains that I don't call her back then, or ever again. Even now, writing this in the middle of the night, and it doesn't matter which night, but it's Halloween, I miss her.

There are people that you love, romantically or platonically, and then that becomes bitter and you can never speak to them again because of the depth of the hurt. And then there are people that you love, romantically or platonically, and you let that person go for no reason at all, just because that's what happens. You and that person simply stop talking and you never start again

There was a day, once, where we dipped our feet into the fountain above the Spanish Embassy in Rome, with a view that went a little more than forever. It was a day so sunny that the idea of cold seemed like fiction. And she looked up at an apartment across the street, and said,

Let's get that place, and live in it together.

There is a life in which that is exactly what we did.

Her name is Jsabelle Pfieffer. Unlike almost everyone else in these entries, that is her actual name. She is from Switzerland. If you run into her, please tell her to get in touch.

Memories of repetition, of remembering, of forgetting, of boredom, of ruins, of fear

New York. Three years into an office job. The view outside is of buildings or a landscape or the sky.

It has been almost four years since I was a college dropout spending all my savings finding places that guidebooks told me to find, and I am now both less obnoxious and less happy. My days are like my yesterdays, and the days before that. But you know this story. It is likely your own.

Most of my life exists in future tense now, and my plans are delineated between those that might actually happen and those that definitely will not. There is the plan to release this book, for instance. But also the plan to buy a car and drive around the country for a few years, searching for that version of me who, in blissful ignorance, thought he had discovered something just by not being home anymore.

I have an Excel sheet to fill out and save into a folder where it will never be opened.

But I also have a walk to take through a summer park or a winter puddle on an avenue. And the dogs in the dog park still are happy, and I'm happy watching them.

Memories of water, of intoxication, of love, of places I never thought I'd be, of islands

Long Beach Island, New Jersey. I am reading on the patio, and listen: They were right, whoever and whenever they were, the people who believed that the universe was a series of nested hollow spheres. Because I can see them now, from this patio. In the center of the spheres is me, and Meg, and beer. Some of the beer is in the bottle and some is in my mouth and in my throat and some is already in my mood. Her voice is a buzz and a beam of light.

Around us is the sphere of wood, in which the patio and the patio furniture and a vegetable shout of bamboo next to us live. This is the sphere that supports. We lean into it drunkenly. Its sense is touch. We feel the grain and rough against our backs.

After that is the sphere of dirt. The soil, and the leafy plants, and the droning insect choir, and the island itself, sloping out of the water and back to water again. This is the sphere that calms. Its sense is smell. I smell the dirt and plants and the island itself. It is a mute giant, using the only language it has to remind me that meaning is unlikely, and unnecessary. Odor of a world in which I never was, and in which all my problems are as gone as I am.

I will do this as long as possible. Living, I mean.

Finally, the sphere of sky. The air and the clouds and the light by which I see everything else. This is the sphere that elevates. From above, this island is a wisp of land.

I know this because there is a framed satellite photo of it hung in a bedroom of this house in which everything, walls, beds, floors, ceilings, is blue. More color than house. The sense of this sphere is sight, of course.

So: I am lying on my back in a patio chair, reading a book, drinking a beer, next to a house I will sleep in, near water I have swam in, surrounded by a garden, under a sky more vast than I had imagined, exactly as vast as I had hoped. Another beer, then? Yes, I think so.

WHAT DOES IT MEAN TO BE A GROWN-UP?

DATA!

Average life span in years: 77.9

Average life span in days: 28,452.39

"Only one thing made him happy

and now that it was gone

everything made him happy."

—*Leonard Cohen,*
Book of Longing

"My life can be best summed up as a revolving door that leads to the different ages of me. Sometimes I am five, full of wonder and awe. Sometimes I am twelve, bursting at the seams with energy, lacking any grace or eloquence. There are times when I am nineteen, eager and ready to take on the world, still awkward, still painfully inexperienced.

What does it mean to be a grown-up? It's a mystery to me. I'm fifty yet rarely act that way. I suspect being a grown-up has something to do with shaving every day (EVERY DAY!) and putting things back where they belong. I might find out when I die. If I do, I'll make sure my dying words are, 'Oh, right. I get it now.'"

—*Timmy, 50, button-down bohemian*

THE GIVING CAR

BY JOEY RIZZOLO

Once there was a 1990 Buick Century, and she loved a little boy. Every day the boy would wash the car and vacuum its imitation leather seats and accompany the car on trips, and, when he was tired, he would sleep at her wheel. The boy loved the car very much. And the car was happy. One day, the boy came to the car and the car said,

"Come boy, vacuum my seats, wax my exterior, and sleep at my wheel."

But the boy said,

"I am too busy for that. I need a blowjob."

"I cannot give you a blowjob safely. But take my imitation leather backseat. There, you may share its delights with a woman."

And the boy did. And the car was happy. And one day the boy came and said,

"Giving Car, I need a job job."

"I cannot give you a job, boy. But I can provide you with transportation to whatever job you desire."

And the boy, dissatisfied with all available jobs, decided to go into business for himself.

"Giving Car, I need a cargo bay in which to store my tools and lumber."

"I do not have a cargo bay, but use my trunk and any other available space."

And the boy did, and in doing so eradicated the interior when he tried to use the car to store muriatic acid. And the car was happy.

"Giving Car, I need to get to the East Village every weekend to perform in *Too Much Light Makes the Baby Go Blind*, but I can't rely on street parking downtown, and I can't afford a garage."

"Then you can park me in the gang center of New Jersey, boy, and take a train from there."

And the boy did. And the car was happy, if missing a few hubcaps.

"Giving Car, I need cash."

"I'm afraid I don't have cash, boy. But ignore the 'check brakes' light on the dashboard as long as you like, and save the money you would have otherwise spent fixing me."

And the boy did. And the car was happy. Until...

"Giving Car, I need to be able to stop when I push on the brake pedal."

"Oh. I'm afraid I can't do that anymore. But trade me in for a sum, with which you can buy another car that can stop whenever you like."

"But you're worthless. You're dented and rusted, you cannot stop, your interior has eroded, and your ceiling is held together with safety pins."

"Gee. I wonder if you couldn't have cared for me just a little better."

Time went by, and the boy stopped visiting the car altogether, even though it was parked on the street right in front of his house. Eventually the boy got another car.

"Giving Car, I need a place to park my newly acquired 2004 Hyundai Elantra."

"I cannot provide you with a parking space, but have me towed away, and let the Hyundai use mine."

And the boy did. And the boy was happy. And the car was gone.

Don't worry about it. It's just a fucking car. Jesus.

STAGES OF GROWTH
AN EXHAUSTIVELY RESEARCHED CHART

Birth Year	Male, Age 15	Female, Age 15	Male, Age 25
1850	Just promoted to assistant manager of sweatshop!	Married and pregnant.	Working 7 days a week to support his 5 children.
1900	Lies about age to go fight in a war or gets hired as a (non-Donald Trump) apprentice.	Isn't married yet, but is being taught manners and how to put up with her future husband's bullshit.	Has his wife and kids, complains about that annoying "Jazz music" all the "kids" are listening to.
1950	Still in school but thinking about what career he wants to pursue.	Doodling hearts on her binder in History class.	Is either married or engaged, has a job and an apartment.
2000	Plays video games in his room.	Texting, "OMG DID U C WHUT MEGAN WUZ WEARING 2DAY WHAT A SLUT!!!"	Plays video games in his room.

BY KEVIN BOWEN

Female, Age 25	Male, Age 35	Female, Age 35
Taking care of children, sewing, and churning butter for fun.	Dead due to working like a slave for 20 years straight.	Is a proud grandmother! And a widow.
Cooks, cleans, takes care of a baby or two.	Works, goes home, smokes a pipe, and listens to wife bitch about ironing.	When not bitching about how much work ironing is, mostly fantasizes about hats.
Is either married or getting really nervous because she's approaching old maid status.	Probably doing cocaine since it's the mid-'80s.	Taking a bunch of kids to soccer practice.
Just finished college, working an unpaid internship, getting hit on by vastly older male boss. Mom and dad pay her rent.	Moved out of parents' house 3 years ago, dating a 22-year-old but actively avoiding things getting too "serious."	After a string of failed relationships with unreliable man-children, researches pregnancy options on Internet during work hours.

WHAT DOES IT MEAN TO BE A GROWN-UP?

"Being a grown-up is about awareness, acceptance, and stability. Mainly personal awareness and acceptance, paired with financial stability.

I don't mean you need to be a model human being. On the contrary, if you are aware you are an evil villain and accept that you are an evil villain, you will probably set evil villain goals and your work towards those goals will be rewarding*.

I also don't mean you need to be rich. Knowing what resources you have and how to use them well is as important as having resources. It will keep you out of debt**, and in a position to command the course of your future.

Being a grown-up is also about change***, which follows quickly on the heels of awareness, acceptance, and stability. As a kid your world is small (or at least smaller). As you become more aware of the larger world, that changes. As soon as you accept that change, a new change occurs. And as soon as you accept the changing nature of the world, you will feel a sense of stability. Which will probably be disrupted again by a change greater than you could imagine.

*For the writer, factors of nature and nurture in becoming an evil villain are very much in debate.

**The writer is terrified of debt. To her, debt is a $50 credit card balance. Her student loans are enough to make her hide in a closet.

***The writer is highly uncomfortable with change and has a hard time dealing with it, denoting she probably could not be described as a 'grown-up.'"

—*Lauren, 26, artist*

DATA! Percentage of average human life that is childhood: 23

PORTRAIT

OF
A LITTLE
TOWN NEAR THE
TOP OF MASLOW'S PYRAMID

BY EEVIN HARTSOUGH

A man opens a fancy deli and catering business. He hosts gourmet sit-down dinners
once a month.

A woman works for a park, managing the cleaning and restoration of an architectural landmark.

A man investigates new ways to help teachers teach better. He pursues screen-writing after hours.

A woman designs hats, sweaters, scarves, gloves. She teaches knitting once a week, in the evenings.

A couple has a baby. They have a home and maybe a pet. They work and they love one another.

You wake up, eat some food, go some place, do something.

And you.

And you.

And you.

And we have goals that are big or small.
And we succeed or we don't.
Little gems of lives, twinkling more or less brightly.

We squint our eyes one way, and they are huge,
all encompassing.
We take a step back, and they appear tiny, almost insignificant.
And time is linear, or seems to be, and so on and on and on...

NOTES FOR MY DAD ABOUT GROWING UP

BY LEAH NANAKO WINKLER

When your wife calls you in tears and gives you the news, *"Sob... Um. Robert? Sob...I'm...sob pregnant? Sobsob,"* you decide to bring roses. As you hold her hard against you in the hospital parking lot near the ambulances, you see:

A flash!

- Holding your wife's matted hair back as she vomits yellow and green.

Another flash!

- Her sexy belly, the one that protrudes just half an inch over her skintight denims, growing bigger and bigger and bigger...

And flash flash flash flash!

- The tiny person you helped create tumbling out of the soppy tired vagina of the woman you love and joining this beautiful world! Life. Will. Be. Good.

Over the next three months you:

[X] Stop smoking/injecting drugs into your body

[X] Decide on the name Jeremy (nickname: Jere-Chan)

[X] Begin teaching English lessons to local salary men who often travel on business to your homeland, a.k.a., The United States Of America!

After saving approximately 95533.0942 yen from this job, you settle into a rented townhouse with pink windows on top of a hill in Shichirigahama. Though you're taller than everyone else in Japan, standing at six foot six inches, peering downhill toward the rocky dirt path on the porch of a home you pay for in a foreign country further justifies your manhood. Feeling empowered by the evolving distance between you and the days of no money = hitchhiking = sleeping on the beach under box roofs = working odd jobs = boozing = acid = tripping = aimless depression / sexing / depression cycle, you lose yourself in a daydream of setting a good example for your child. You will be kind. You will go to work. You will make hotcakes for brunch on Sundays. When Jere-Chan approaches adolescence = hormones = backlash and isolation, he will gravitate toward rather than resent his family, much due to your well-practiced role of the ex-hippie cool Dad who is strong, hilarious and rich with life experiences.

"I saw your mama sittin' on a bench in Berkeley with Aunt Ayako. Couldn't understand anything they were saying," you'd joke. "Just knew I wanted to take one of them home. Sure as hell didn't care which one though."

As Jere-Chan would crack a smile and roll his eyes, you'd renege the jest and give reassurance that it was his mama, Miyoko, who caught your eye from the beginning.

"I love your mama. You know that."

It was true. The moment you saw Miyoko sitting on that bench under the California sun, laughing uninhibitedly with her crooked teeth, you saw record stores+sweet letters+showing her your little possessions like the antique clock hanging on the wall of your studio apartment that once belonged to your father who took care of cows on a far away farm in the land of the free. She'd say *sugoi* (neat!) and together you'd get high and go to free rock concerts and sing reggae while lying naked on your twin-sized bed with no sheets.

After your third date, Miyoko became yours, and any weight of purposelessness previously harbored on your back disappeared into her kind lips, generous thighs, and smooth yellow white skin that enveloped her breasts, safely carrying her dark perky nipples you so loved to lick. As this precious time slipped away like the red silky robe you stripped off of Miyoko on lazy evenings, you one day found yourself casually conducting a marriage proposal.

During a routine drive home following completion of an errand you no longer remember, you asked, "Wanna get married?"

To which she replied, "OK."

That same afternoon your non-American citizen fiancé received a deportation notice from the INS. You eloped in Reno the next day, both of you in jeans. In the hotel room lobby, your tipsy new wife made an international call to her father and you heard him crying through the phone receiver after she exclaimed, "Daddy! I just got married. To an American!" A few weeks later after he'd cooled and gave his blessing, you and Miyoko, despite previous valiant efforts to stay in the USA as a couple, traveled to Japan on his dime. Stepping off of that plane into a country you never thought you'd live in, you realized how your escape from Ohio, where there was nothing but miles of grass and cows and your mama tying you to a tree and whipping you when you were bad, had finally culminated.

Three Japanese Things You Saw and Loved

Mount Fuji (climbed it but couldn't get to the top)

Cherry trees (rained pink petals onto Miyoko's shiny black hair)

Ojijo-san statues (lined the corners of random streets you could not pronounce)

Three Japanese Foods You Ate and Loved

Dried fish snacks (including dried squid with cheese)

Peko-Chan Milky Candy (milk-flavored caramel by Fujiya Co.)

Eel (tastes like a combination of mushrooms and the sea)

Three Japanese Things You Drank and Loved

Asahi Fujisan (solid pilsner)

Lipovitan D (a 100ml bottle of taurine and caffeine)

Milk (the best you'd ever had)

At the end of your trip, you asked Miyoko how she felt about not going back. She shrugged, and you knew that she knew that you needed to stay. Being an adult is fucking hard, but here, at least, you were beginning to feel like yourself.

A year went by.

Then another.

And then it's:

AUGUST 5, 1985

In the delivery room, the doctors inform you of Jere-Chan's lady parts! Surprise! Your visions and expectations of having a son are shattered and Miyoko looks like Jell-O. Then, after fourteen hours of rigor and labor, I—a silent baby human girl—am pulled out of your wife along with a mixture of slime and blood. Because I'm not breathing, they transport me to the ICU via glass incubator. It's raining outside. Miyoko starts to weep. Before you know it, you're in tears too, and for the first and last time, you cry together, holding each other through the hurt. You have no idea that although you'll endure plenty of pain throughout your marriage, this kind of closeness will never happen between you two again. Not when you run out of money, not during the birth of your second daughter, and not even during the deaths of your parents or her parents or your best friend, Jeff.

THE NEXT SIX YEARS

After visiting me in my incubator every day for two weeks, you can hold me. After three weeks, you take me home. That first night, you bathe and feed me and, before you know it, you're watching me grow. After I learn to crawl, I learn to walk, and, one unexpected morning, I run up with excitement to knee you in the balls because I don't know what the bulge in between your legs could possibly be, other than toys to kick.

You scream in pain, but don't get mad. I am inconsolable for the rest of the day. That is the last memory I have of you before things started to change. Before we moved to America, and before you went insane.

TODAY

Last night I had a nightmare where you ripped all of mom's hair out and I had to console her by gluing it strand by strand back onto her scalp. After I finished, I tried to choke you but your neck was too strong. Today is your birthday. I can't call because it makes me nauseous. So I will write a note I will never send:

APRIL 24, 2010

Hey Dad,

I found out about the "incident" you had with my sister last month when you hit her in the face and chased her with your car. What happened to you in between now and those days when you'd let us ride on the back of your bike in Hiroba Co-En and laugh when we'd complain that your butt was too big for the three of us?

Three Memories of You I Am Saddened by After We Moved to America

Screaming fits (sometimes daily for hours, often about our menstrual cycles)

Asking us if we wanted anything from the store when your fits were over (substitute for an apology)

Your attempt to switch to non-alcoholic beer (24-packs of Bud Light to Buckler then Bud Light again)

Three Disturbing Thoughts I Have About You Now

Fantasies of your death (I see you lifeless in a coffin and the persistent pain in my shoulder diminishes)

Images of you touching yourself (wondering if you do it, to see if you're a human)

Worrying that you are going to kill my mom and sister (and I can't be there to help them)

Three Things I Wish I Could Tell You, Now that I'm an Adult

I know I'm far away but you're even farther.

Please let me get you some help because you cannot continue living this way.

You are still my father and I love you.

What I'm Doing Right Now, in Case You Were Worried

APRIL 14, 2011

Right now I am sitting on a dirty bench at the 4th Avenue stop in South Slope, waiting for a Queens bound R train. I will transfer to the N (or the Q if it's still running to Astoria) at Atlantic Avenue. At this moment in time I am a good girl who does not cheat, tease, or lie. I did my taxes this year, and for the first time in a while, I am getting a refund.

APRIL 29, 2011

Right now I am on the train and reflecting on the rehearsal I just conducted.

I Paid

$24 for rehearsal space

A $15 equipment fee that had previously expired

$5.80 for a post rehearsal Number 3 Value Meal at McDonald's (two cheeseburgers, fries, a Dr. Pepper)

$2.25 each way on the subway

APRIL 30, 2011

Right now I have an increasing awareness that my body is going to fall apart someday.

MAY 2, 2011

Right now I am realizing that I might be the annoying one.

MAY 14, 2011

Right now I am afraid that I can't do all the things I use to do. Or all the things I like to say I can do.

EVERY DAY

I Am

Recognizing patterns

Trying to break those patterns

Being awed by the self-destructive streaks of myself and others

Appreciating the help of others

Learning how to take care of myself

Crying about the daunting task of actually doing exactly that

Learning to break up with boys who aren't good for me

Learning how to break up with friends who aren't good for me

Learning to hold on to the ones who are

Saying I'm OK

Being OK

Other Things You Don't Know About Me

I am in love and I want my lover to stay with me always. I hope he is never in a terrible car accident or infected with a terminal illness. I hope he never stops thinking I am beautiful and smart.

I want a giant dog that could be mistaken for a bear, and I want that dog to bark at those who are mean and snuggle against those who are nice.

I want a small kitten who meows while riding on that dog's back.

I want to have a husband someday and maybe children. Together we will settle down in a happy home near the water.

I want a nice lamp.

I want labels for my files and cabinets for those files with labels on them.

I want to do household accounting on Sundays with my future husband while sipping coffee.

I want to go into the city for meetings.

I want to have a treadmill inside of the house.

I want my friends to be healthy, kind, and compassionate and forgiving of my ego.

I want my mother to stop crying.

I want you to be happy.

I want.

WHAT DOES IT MEAN TO BE A GROWN-UP?

DATA!

Average age of US prison population: 39

DATA!

Average age of US policeman: 39

DATA!

Year of first US child labor law: 1916 (overturned 2 years later)

Year of first successful US child labor law: 1938

"All growth is a leap in the dark, a spontaneous unpremeditated act without benefit of experience. Every sign of growth is a revolt against death."

—*Henry Miller*, "The Wisdom of the Heart"

mint wafers on the moon

mint wafers on the moon ≠ creativity
   equal "problem solving"
are font too big
are mornings i wake up with an intensity saying
most people on the planet are americans   most people on the planet are Americans, the pious the recondite
the spiritual needs of one man's neighbor one woman's neighbor one palm moisture to pocket along
and dai is dependence   the web(naked) camera(girl) tells me so a beautiful retreating
down the hallway of her family's refurbished Victorian flat   , ha ! What a Familial Clamor it raised
to her father saying   HELLO MY NAME IS:
                    apparatus

and i want your daughter to be a gladness for me.
i want her to recognize the genuine spiral of history as it pulls us into big picture insignificance. our parceled suffering makes us mythological, given the day each day anew nailed to a board pasted with flaking black parchment paper. a generation unparalleled in purposelessness and each outdoing the one previous in silent screaming bred from the spectacular. thus their mouths womb it without their knowing. "Use what your understanding understands to nurture that which your understanding does not understand." so please observe how we garden our panic on the back of the sunk-shouldered son of fourwinds heavenearth.

and if the writing wants to be a paragraph, let it
and if it wants to be a stanza, let it
if unintentionality, then it will be so
if "personal expression" then that too.
art comes from the inward for you
for others they open their eyes and are simply being-in-now.

then how long since i have seen a city at dawn?
when since the traffic over the river causeway a tweed hat wears
or birds flying their reflections across the polished floor—
light's unrest warms interview table minute by minute—

by
bryan zubalsky

while the Lord troubles my mind
with visions of CREMAINS CREMAINS CREMAINS
and

      CHARLIE ROSE

                            CHARLIE ROSE

                                                  CHARLIE ROSE

, the truest perhaps discussion that is not going on at this present moment
he is nonetheless the finest dressed eidolon of interjection available
to our wholly currant mind of dim.

[TO BE READ BRISKLY IN MONOTONE]
birds reflection floor
table minutes light-warms-light
Troubled Lord
visions city Charlie at dawn
[—CUT TAPE HERE—]

[TO BE READ MONOTONOUSLY BUT BRISK]
traffic hat tweed bridge river
times transversal moving wing
Lord sight Cremains
unsure unsaid ideal him dress
[—CUT TAPE HERE—]

—resume, with parity. documentation of studio where bodies at last at rest at music tore. at that time my complaints were petty, my jealousy apparent in their aims and concerns. to blame: the tyrannical primacy of images on the internet. as for why i've never written theory, that takes a belief in one's own authority which i never cared to have. i ask earnestly What were you like as a child? You were young once and now I've seen you without clothes on, strange the way time demarcates your coming into hello. but never a dull moment, chewing seaweed, cooking soup for one, taking the scholastic exams to become a multifaceted genius of the late Ming and author of the Yaodi pao Zhuang, that unsung mythopiece of inner chapter commentary. And if what "I" does is important, then to whom, and relative to what? Books on the mantelpiece, friends never call, questions of Art and Life and sitting under a low table. All absence is you. Father is a loud narrow but mother is warm chuckling wool. In the experience of water made new, lysergic debates the philosopher on his deathbed.

His westbed, his deathwit.

vast winds across the plains blow me back to a dream of thin
affections. i don't wear a
        suit.
                i never knew anything good.

    is cat crying?

is space on a page just a jerkaround?   is bryan writing?   is a dog in heaven?

        Ophiuchus my favorite constellation, how have you been   these
students pore over the yellowed pages of star atlases

seeking the power of the line.

            What wisdom comes with age is tacit

            while the heart remains

                a song of frenzy.

    and if i disappeared tomorrow life would go on just so, just so.

            no panic.

                    just one small man

                            passing off the self as individuated fun.

compassion adust.   lolly candy.

    "is why-am brightening?"   is too short life, is learning dying

        is well to do so.   three years from thirty is not grown up.
        posterity desires is not grown up.

                the way you look in that skirt   Phwoar!
        is just a mind-state
        but o how beautiful to feel!   if just for a moment
        the skin cries "obbligato!"

        and we understand this to be love.

in bed we
talk about book
activate erogenous zonez
the t.v. show gets big
bigger and bigger!
we are living in the t.v. show   luminous dream   listening to:

                                                              post-sound con-kret

                                                              a

                                                                              a   }

                                                              outer-parén theses

                                                              ;____; <---- a crying face

                                                              banging on a trashcan

                    '   '

              '   '

                          '   '

                                                              =^ . ^=   now a cat face

                    future sounds to presage the Great Death Happening
                         or Death Event, the names are unclear.

                                        103

i go out wandering the North Lakes with madness
lost my shadow against the bright white background
lived in the wild lonely places
reckoning my cumulative hours of saying mhmm to the phone
i meet you in the t.v. show shaded woodland
where you plank on me nakedly. this i like
and am glad.
behold i have grown a mushroom that is also a cat
the dream of mycologists
soon whole palaces and sacred structures of fungus built
and you can't stop it.
we put ritual in this space
without binding it to the triune of dimensions
patterning instead a psychosituational space
to set Ocean's boundary.
Purpose will sanctify this round.
Use will justify its being.

Cheops Amata tell: if technology advances & i don't submit
how will i make my lucre?
left holding the brain in a bit of plastíque
while Death proves Its majesty every day.

[img - Her Glass Ondine Body In The Bath]

"Mirrors dont reflect anything.
Tests with mirrors showed they
do not even reflect x-rays.
Conclusion:
They do not re-direct Chi."

Yes.

i am often afraid

in the mid houre of the night

the horse in the radio comes barking terra jazz

tender perennials

we are

the high roads of spring. radionuclide migration.

"the froth of human wit,
excrements of curiosity"

and in dreams i am still in college.

Q: poore scholar
what haue you to yr name?

A: a paper on the Material Reality of the Vulva

Whatever you want to happen continues to not happen. Meaning & purpose are elusive. Flat affect threatens. Lucky numbers are

approach for your epiphany
you are blessed
there is an obligation to others
there is a breath to end your breath.

awareness.   awareness.   awareness!

i am drawn thru some manner of intrigue and persist, greatly diminished.

it rewrites itself, as does everything.
everything makes a five and a six.

hope you are all right
forgot what i wanted to say
reading about gardening
planning the garden
all animals are fellow animals
reading seed catalogs two thousand eleven.

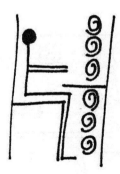

AN OPEN LETTER TO MY MOM

BY NATHAN RABIN

Dear mom,

I turned thirty-five not too long ago. You might not have noticed. We had some times there, now didn't we? Me in the womb. You carrying me. The delivery. Blood and guts and placenta everywhere. You strapping me into my car seat when you took me away from my dad for what I may or may not have thought was the last time.

I tend to linger on those moments because they're all I have. You fucking abandoned me, mom. I never stopped hurting. Somehow the pain seems to get worse with time when it should be getting better. I know. I should have gotten over it by now. Throughout my life I've told myself that I've gotten over it, that I have forgiven you and moved on. The older I get, the more I realize that it's not the kind of thing you ever really get over. It's the primordial wound, ma. The one that doesn't go away.

I'm not right, mom. I'm not sure I ever have been. I'm broken. I'm fragile. I'm delicate. I require excessive hugs. Everything about me is at least a little bit off. My voice irritates people. I scare people with my intensity. I don't know what to do with my hands. I have difficulty looking people in the eyes. I scare people with my vulnerability and desperate need to be loved. I have a hard time making friends.

I don't sleep right. I worry. I drink too much and need to smoke pot to fall asleep. I'm on anti-depressants now and probably always will be. I cry sometimes for no reason at all. I don't eat right. I don't walk right. I don't stand right. I get nervous and shy and I stammer and I have a hard time talking to people. Even the people I love most have difficulty understanding me.

I finally found a woman that I love, mom. But it took me thirty-three years, a whole lot of anti-depressants, therapy, and bad relationships to get to a place where I could trust women enough to give of myself completely. Before I met Cadence, I didn't trust relationships. I didn't trust marriage. I didn't trust anything, because you betrayed my trust, mother. You were supposed to care for me. You were supposed to love me. You didn't.

I've led an amazing fucking life, mom. I wrote a whole fucking book about the desperate and sad things I did to try to fill the hole in my soul that should have been filled by a mother's love. There's so much I wish I had been able to share with you. I've spent my lifetime trying to impress people because I do not think I am worthy of being loved. I've tried to impress people with my words and ideas and conceits because I could never and I can never impress you because you just aren't fucking there, are you? You are eternally consistent in your absence.

I'm a man now, mom. For the first time in my life, I take that seriously. I have a home and a woman I love and a job and a family to protect. Since you've never listened to me, and I've never been able to reach you. I thought you might like to know that, now that I am a man, I will nevertheless still always be a sad little boy desperately crying out for a mother's love, knowing full well the futility of the gesture.

Nathan Rabin

WHAT DOES IT MEAN TO BE A GROWN-UP?

"Being a grown-up means having a better understanding of the world, but also having the wisdom to know you will never understand all.

Being a grown-up also means you shouldn't like playing with Legos anymore, but you probably still do."

—Jinjoo, 28, business student

"It means realizing that every character Ethan Hawke played in the '90s was not, in fact, world-weary and wise, but a pretentious dick."

—Yashoda, 27, researcher, muckraker

DATA!

Average age of world population

1950: 23.9

2000: 26.8

2050: 37.3 (projected)

WE ADD A PINCH OF CAYENNE WHILE IT'S BOILING DOWN

BY VERONICA LIU

I'm right at that point during vacation when familyness is overwhelming me in that way, so that all I want to do is ask Will to marry me because we're obviously going to be happy 'til we're old and shrunken and still making ginger tea when coming down with something, like that couple in their late seventies I saw the other day on the 1 train, the day Will left for Michigan. I was sitting in the sweet seat, the one against the wall in the two-seater, and this couple ambles in: an Asian woman and a white man, neither attractive nor unattractive, just remarkably short, he a bit taller than she, and short like they weren't always like that—not short like they've grown up used to this, like they've had to get used to embracing low views, and looking up, and have thus made their statures somehow bigger or taller as a result—but short like it's sort of new, even if already eight-years new, where they're still figuring out their clothes and their stunted weights and their shortened strides, though thankfully they've both shrunken at the same pace so they're still proportionate to one another in the way they've always been used to—phew! They can still tilt their heads at the same angles they've always done, and kiss at just the right depth of tongue. Their arms can still snake around each other's waists at comple-mentary heights as before, his arm reaching down while hers with more of a bend at the el-bow—but neither out of phase with how it had been the forty or fifty years before. When they lie together, her head can still fit at just the right pocket of his neck, and they can still make each other shriek when one has cold feet because they jumped into bed right after walking from the tiled bathroom floor without socks or slippers. This is the couple who walked onto the 1 train four hours after I said goodbye to Will the morning of his flight to Michigan, two hours after he texted that he'd made the bag check-in cut-off time within a minute of the deadline, one hour after I finally woke up and read that text, one hour before he texted again to tell me that he'd arrived safely in the Midwest and that he loved me. And because the train was a little bit crowded, with both commuters and those December tourists, the Asian woman sat next to me, and the man stood in front of her, facing her. They didn't speak much, but when they did it sounded like inside jokes, mumblings that weren't even necessarily meant to be funny but that made them smile and giggle all the same. The part that killed me around 50th Street was when the man said, "Later, we can go do some Christmas shopping. I gotta get something for my sister. I gotta get ginger"—and here I thought his sister's name was Ginger—"then we can make ginger tea. Does that sound good? When I think I'm coming down with something, I like to make a big pot of ginger tea." And then the woman made a noise—without it being a giggle or a laugh, it still sounded like she thought the man was great, and hilarious, and that ginger tea was the best. And then, with the man holding the pole to his right and leaning in close, the woman lightly whacked him in the crotch of his pea coat, an affectionate jab at his balls, right then and there to my left on the 1 train! And they made sounds again, like they were cooing or giggling or sipping hot ginger tea that hits the spot, and when a seat opened up in the row across from us I moved over to a free one and said the man could sit down next to his lady. And they gave enthusiastic smiles of appreci- ation and kept on, occasionally remarking on something but generally more smiley than chatty, like they didn't need to talk all at once because they'd still be sitting or walking next to each other once they'd leave the train, arms snaked around each other's waists and her head lightly bumping his upper arm, as they pick up some Christmas trinket for his sister and, just before calling it a day, select a meaty branch of ginger root, bulbous arms askew.

ADULT CONTEMPORARY GENIUS LIST

OR

DEATH IN SUMMER/FLIGHT IN FALL

BY KEVIN R. FREE

Before you finish your work, your computer dies. Boo. A baby cries as you press play on your half-alive iPod, and you think, *hear, hear*, as Sammy Davis Jr. sings "I've Gotta Be Me." You try to march in your seat to the music, and you think you see Sammy outside on the wing.

You rub your eyes, the baby cries, and you realize that Sammy's gone; now you see your mother and Black Gal and Michael Jackson and Ellie Greenwich on the wing. Come down now, they say—which is weird, because they're rising up quickly, like they've opened parachutes.

The baby cries some more, and, since this is a waking dream, you step out of the Window of Hope and stand there on the wing with Ed McMahon and Patrick Swayze and E. Lynn Harris, and you look at yourself and yourself looks at you, with your hair blowing in the breeze, and yourself thinks you look great with dreadlocks, even though you think you look like Jar Jar Binks. You look up and make a mental note that Tony Kushner was right, because there they all are—mommy, meemaw, Farrah, Sammy, MJ, even Joni Mitchell's voice—creating a soul net and repairing the ozone.

The baby screams and Josh Groban sings something in Italian. Or Spanish. It doesn't matter because you remember that you can't help repair the ozone. You don't have the tools. You don't have the words. You don't have the Al Jarreau we're-in-this-love-together kind of soul to make it happen. You don't even have hair. And you're never gonna have a baby of your own.

But you do have your iPod, and you'll be OK until even Mariah Carey's voice lets you down. Again.

Your ears pop, and you've come to the Stoney End, and that baby's voice will not be drowned out, and Mama, let me start all over, but it's time to stow the iPod, and you look out the window to find that the dead really are gone, and you've only lost something you never had, though you could have had it if you were different, but you're not different, and Bette believes in you; she wants to deserve you. And that's enough to make the baby stop crying for now.

You laugh because you're happy about it, even though you didn't know that's what you wanted. And you realize the work you haven't finished is work you haven't even begun. Yay.

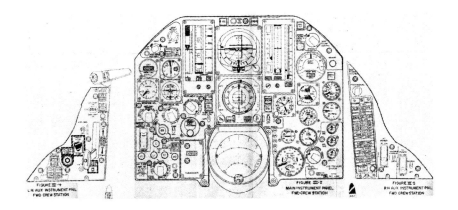

KETCHUP

BY ETAN BERKOWITZ

I can still remember the first time I had a pair of tits to myself. She made me feel completely relaxed. We took it slow. She guided my young, tender lips to her warm bosom and told me it'd be all right. She treated me like a baby because I was one. My mom is a nice and helpful person. She always has been.

Growing up to Jewish parents on the Upper West Side ensured that my baby-toddler-child self would have every precaution taken for him. My parents rounded the corners of all of life's sharp corners. They sanded, rubberized, and bubble wrapped my life so much that it was less living life and more participating in a controlled laboratory experiment run by Dr. Ruth and Woody Allen. (The sex tape was very funny, yet informative.)

The real problem with my childhood was ketchup, that oozing red ambrosia. I would slather that shit on everything from $50 steaks to vegetable quinoa. I was obsessed. When I was in middle school, my parents caught me toasting hot dog buns, slathering on ketchup, and eating them. Not one or two, but five at a time. This weird treat wasn't restricted to my own kitchen. I asked the lovely people at Papaya King to give me a hot dog with everything (extra ketchup, please!), but hold the hot dog. The request was so strange they would give it to me for free. I did this numerous times. I only got the treat sans hot dog because I was kosher at the time due to fear of my ancestors' ghosts. Every Berkowitz before me kept this sacred tradition of avoiding delicious BLTs, lobster rolls, and scallops, so who would I be to venture so boldly?

I blame the scientists watching over me for this sad state of being. When I was younger, I liked ketchup, same as any other kid, but it's not like I would miss class because I was freebasing high fructose corn syrup. It started with my parents. They would call ahead to play dates to make sure there was ketchup for me. Family dinners at my parents' friends' houses weren't complete unless they asked if they had ketchup for me. Oh no? Well, can we ask the neighbors? Because my parents did. They even put ketchup packets in my backpack in case I happened to run into a food that, gasp, was not in a fifty-foot radius of ketchup! It was like reverse diabetes. It made me expect ketchup to appear anytime food was near.

This is a serious case of First World problems, but ketchup was holding me back. Or maybe the neurotic duo hovering above me was. Each child begins their life where their parents put them. Sometimes you start in a modest green house on Baltic Avenue, and sometimes you start by living in a huge red hotel on Boardwalk. My mom's family suffered through the Holocaust. Her mom had an entire family wiped out before she was ever born. She is version 2.0 and Hitler was a dick. I can't help but contrast my grandfather's experience of hiding mini Torahs in the cracks of his bed frame to support his spirit with my hiding ketchup packets in my backpack to support my fat ass. I was a fat kid by the way. Thanks, Mom.

For many years, I expected the hovering gloved hands of my parents to protect me, like I was a big-nosed bowling bowl bouncing off the bumpers of the alley. One of my first experiences leaving the bumper lane was eating bacon. For an Upper West Side Jew, this is akin to spiking Moses' canteen with a laxative right before his trip up Mount Sinai.

A friend and I were reflecting one day by the Hudson about why we were following the tenets of something we never cared about, something that a mere millennia of Jewish tradition and parenting had told us was right. We made sexual innuendos all through morning services and cracked jokes about how Aaron melted the golden calf into golden dildos for the Israelites. We got kicked out of almost every Torah study class. We prayed, kept kosher, and wore little hats only because it was routine. So why were we kosher? Why were we going to synagogue every Saturday? Did we actually care about those things?

Leaving the laboratory and entering the real world is always a shocker. No more gloved hands, sterilized instruments, or meticulous precautions taken, only unprotected experience. Getting mugged, having sex, eating a BLT, or shooting a gun for the first time all bring this tingling sensation of a new experience, and hopefully it's not herpes.

Watching that bacon sizzle in the pan was euphoric. The smell of maple and the crackling of pig fat were a personal bar mitzvah for me, while my parents and the ghosts of my ancestors cried for my soul. No more dictated tenets or holy scrolls, just me and the experience (BLT) I was making. For a brief moment, I floated in an enlightened universe. It was the best meal I've ever had in my life. And the best part? There was no ketchup, only bacon grease.

WHAT DOES IT MEAN TO BE A GROWN-UP?

DATA!

Average age at first marriage in US

	Male	Female
1900:	25.9	21.9
1950:	22.8	20.3
2000:	26.8	25.1
2010:	28.2	26.1

"I was a long time
coming.
I'll be a long time gone.
You've got your whole
life to do something,
and that's not very long."

—*Ani DiFranco, 1993,*
"Willing to Fight"

"Who put all this stuff in
my apartment?

Who put all this ice in
my drink?"

—*Ani DiFranco, 2012,*
"Splinter"

200-HOUR POWER QUEST WEEKEND

BY J CHASTAIN

Doctor Crash slew his only son with falling spike, that he might be reborn as Devil World's supreme opponent. Surgery took two years at the Lab. Kid Crash, Cyborg Hero, moves through the Air Fortress's green steel corridor, then he buys a steak from the machine in his Hotel Room. Plastic bags on the floor contain figurines of tiny howling men with rifles and swords and armor (official MK Brand). The steak is amphibian (official MK Brand). The darkened wallscreen displays a rotating logo: MONSTER KILLERS, MONSTER KILLERS, MONSTER KILLERS. The Air Fortress hangs in black space above a boiled red planet and a giant decal on the side says MONSTER KILLERS. Ships like cattle skulls flood upward, firing teeth and bone shards. Most explode on contact with turret fire except the one that tears into the fortress wall and penetrates the convention space; disembarking skeletons and Battle Witches raze booths and displays while the workers are pulled into hard vacuum, lanyards and badges flapping helplessly. Six hours later the show floor is reopened and video capture of the attack is edited, scored, pay-per-view broadcast through MK CCTV. A man in MK-branded jumpsuit yells into his phone: "It's evolving. It's experiential. It's an open narrative."

Kid Crash wanders back out and upstairs to the Con, browses booths he's already seen, does not get into the long line to meet Max Attacker, Assassin Supreme. In this cavern of light and noise, the new catalog sprawls in every direction. Plastic WarTanx overrun plastic magmamen in a glowing diorama. Full-size WarTanx rotate on a dais. There are submarines and gyros and flamethrowers and chainsaws and telescopic spears and a gauntlet that looks like a cross between Wolverine's claws and a lightsaber. The decals on the side say MONSTER KILLERS. Dudes are trying on helmets. Dudes are trying on space suits. Dudes are trying out bladed boomerangs. Dudes are checking out optical implants. Dudes are getting their spines replaced with more expensive spines. Fluid is dripping down Kid Crash's forearm. In the bathroom mirror, his gleaming green body armor is cracking and separating at the shoulder. The biomass underneath leaks. Chevrons streak across his field of vision, settle on the Space Spider flattened in the ceiling corner. Floating white text says it's worth "50." He kills it. Floating graphics say his MK account's been credited with "50." Then they freeze, turn dark, hover like burn-in while he rubs his eyes. He sits in a toilet stall when he realizes the plate-mounted sensory apparatus has started pulling away from his face to reveal a scrambled mess that hasn't developed as much as mutated since infancy. Kid Crash, Cyborg Hero, is outgrowing his implants and typing calculations for the coming grinds. One hundred hours? Two hundred hours? Two hundred hours shooting pterodactyls generated by the egg crater. Two hundred hours collecting the garbage they drop. Two hundred hours' worth of credit in the account, but time is suddenly starting to feel like time. Two hundred hours pulling the trigger. Two hundred hours thinking about anything or anywhere else. Something's changed since the days, five minutes ago, he was toddling through the lands surrounding the periwinkle dome of Crash's Lab, fighting grinning sharks and voodoo masks and polar bears. The cell on the spreadsheet says two hundred hours.

A floating, flickering, white "10,000" warns of the mummy's approach. He shoots it before it can get its hands around his throat and, back on the floor, watches the text floats blink out as eager combatants shoot the shit out of the new wave of invaders and the black coffins that glide behind them. Some time later he's on a drop ship crowded with drunk, excited men all loading the new MK guns and reading the new MK books and trying the new MK apps, their faces concealed by branded helmets (bubbly or angular).

MONSTER KILLERS

MONSTER KILLERS

MONSTER KILLERS

MONSTER KILLERS

MONSTER KILLERS

The planetary surface buzzes with bugs of war. Stragglers from the fleet of Gorgonized bone-ships still erupt from canyons, shooting toward their enemy in the sky. The dropship crashes down in dense, fleshy jungle and everyone's plastic bracelets list the time for the return trip. Monster Killers run over the land shooting everything in sight, getting stabbed, getting back up, screaming, throwing grenades, getting poisoned, chugging energy drinks, chugging antivenin, shooting steroids, shooting each other, digging for treasure, climbing ladders, building forts, fortifying bases, being dragged screaming into underground caverns. Only the Crash Module can detect the 8 Power Gems of Devil World, of which only two remain to be collected; Kid Crash jet bikes east toward the red desert mesas where Gem Power radiates, blasting Terror Birds that feed along the way. The cacti uproot themselves and open dripping eyeball blooms, flex their muscles, and give chase. Colossal stone hands emerge from sand. The pyramids are crawling steadily forward, revealing vital organs as they eject bricks to squash prey. Condors eat carnivorous flies. Air Sharks eat condors. Thundering clouds consume sharks. Kid Crash's Nuclear Blaster clears the monster mass blocking the entrance shaft to the Golden Temple, where ramps and corridors slope farther and farther down into the dark, illuminated only by helmet lamp. This is a bad place for rocket boots to crack and malfunction, but they do. Getting around takes forever without a double jump, and things are in pursuit—moving walls with grinning mouths, masked hounds, creeping blood fountains. The lowest floors are flooded and the water's rising, and a slick black snake, featureless, miles long, is probing for prey. In a deep alcove, Kid Crash rips the slap-on bracelet off his wrist and tosses it to the ground. A beige window extends to the ceiling and a humanoid face, grinning, white, instantly loads MK SHOP, the endless menu of branded field gear. Draining the account by half for the brand new MK-AQUASSAULT kit is preferable to drowning; a white arm drops it on the ground and then the arm is gone, and the window is gone. Kid Crash, newly equipped, jets into a colossal, flooded cavern filled with centuries of murk and corpse debris, ancient skulls floating like platforms on the water's surface, water seeping into the cracks in his shell. Up on the shore, a long hallway branches towards Gem Power, but a monolithic coffin is in the intersection, floating two feet off the ground. It twitches in his vision, ghosting. Water trickles from the sides of his face-plate, which begins to slide and droops, ripped free by gravity, clattering to the ground. The coffin pirouettes, and Kid Crash is scooped up after a thirty-second sprint, and the heavy lid slams shut.

Loud-ass harpsichords and pipe organs play in the dark valley. Coffins glide up craggy rock bridges to the great labyrinth of the Castle, still launching attack ships. The portcullis closes and Kid Crash is dumped onto the checkered tile floor of a great entry hall hung with rotting red curtains. All of the people of the hall, witches and muckmen and mermen and enormous spiders, are coming and going. The swollen blue mush in his skull's orbits can display no values, no objectives, no cash balances. Kid Crash is starving for context, but there is none; even the Map and Gemventory screens stored in his memory are inaccessible. In this situation, it is natural to be chased by skeletons. They go up the grand staircase, through all the wings of the second and third and fourth and fifth and sixth and seventh floors, into all the hiding places behind ornate, ruined furniture and within galleries of destroyed marble statuary. They chase as fast or as slowly as the exhausted Crash can crawl, clacking their jaws. Steam rises from boiling goo pits in a rocky cavern below the sub-basements, and Dracula is here, still the most valuable in the MK Bestiary. Dracula is talking to somebody. Dracula is trying to explain things: there are ballrooms and dining rooms and kitchens and larders but there are no shops in Castle of Dracula. Dracula says that humans have potential, best revealed by reduction to their component elements. Kid Crash, wheezing, is shoved into burning goo. His shell snaps apart and the soft thing inside rapidly dissolves. The only real change is that the new thing forming understands that it's dead, will always be dead. Checklists and charts and graphs and cash balances evaporate. It's two hundred hours in the pits, and time is ceasing to feel like time. The thing that emerges slaps its fins on mossy stones and looks at the patterns etched by erosion in the walls and sees the snapping, carnivorous ferns in the corner and is bewildered to realize it never had a clue how any of this stuff works. It sleeps in pools of mud. It sleeps in a haunted four-poster bed. It catches its reflection in the mirror and recalls that it's worth "5,000" to somebody else. Great chains anchoring the Castle yank free from the ground as it rises into the air and out of the atmosphere. Its turrets and walls and towers are shifting, reconfiguring, as the Air Fortress's automated systems are cataloging, labeling, packaging them. In twenty minutes, it's a scale model for sale on the show floor. Hungover, armored men watch plastic MK BATTLEWASP and MK FANGBIRD space fighters fire projectiles at its battle damage triggers and wonder what part this chapter plays in the epic personal quests that describe their lives. Then the station is overwhelmed and on fire and everyone is piled into cruisers for the long, slow trip back up the freeway.

CAPTIVE ZOMBIE SNAKE

BY CARA FRANCIS

In the cab on the way home from work, Conan is on. I'm sharing the cab with one of the other bartenders who lives in the neighborhood, and he taps on the screen to turn it off, but it just comes right back on again. Conan has a giant yellow snake curled around his neck and the neck of a man standing next to him who seems to be in charge of the snake. The snake has its head tucked just under Conan's crotch, so it kind of looks like Conan has a giant yellow snake dick that is also beginning to choke him. And I think to myself: yeah right. Yeah right, just right now that happened. By chance. The snake just had to get up in Conan's crotch and make it look like he has a giant snake for a dick. On camera. In a room full of captivated people.

Then there's a snake dick close up and I say that stupid snake is trained, and the other bartender I am sharing a cab with says it's not even a snake. It's a zombie snake. In an aquarium all day, subject to constant fondling, fangs cut out, doesn't have to hunt, barely even knows the smell of its own shit. They're like dolls. They're like dolls, their teeth ripped out, their nuts ripped off, and I say to him I guess we have to take away their instinct the way we took away our own, as we pass a Calvin Klein billboard high up.

I hate Calvin Klein in the sky that simulates a god. I hate my vibrator that simulates a fuck and my computer that simulates friends. He says that's good, you should write that down. And I say I won't forget it, but now I'm trying to get it out and it's not the same as when I said it that first time and meant it, because right after I say I won't forget it I look out the window at an enormous apartment building that looks like one of those manmade beehives and say: It's so bleak though. Maybe I should forget it. And then I do.

This barely says what I want it to. I gnaw on my pillows with baby teeth. When did we decide that if we're going to be this way everything else has to be too? When we named the animals?

Conan, you're fucked. You're stuck in a television being choked to death by a captive zombie snake. Acting like it's a surprise. You are a captive zombie snake.

And most of the world would be you if they got the chance.

ONCE UPON...

BY MARCY BRAIDMAN

Once upon a time there was a small girl who lived in a large castle.

She did not know how long she had been there or if she had a family somewhere missing her. She shared the castle with her large dog, who was nameless, just like her.

Every morning she tied up her long red hair, leapt out of the huge bed, and went downstairs to prepare her breakfast. She ate eggs that had been laid by her own chickens, cooked in oil from olives that she had picked and pressed. Her tea was brewed from leaves that she had grown and sweetened with milk she had squeezed and honey she had harvested. The land that her castle sat in the middle of was vast, fruitful, and hers alone to work. She had no knowledge or memories beyond it.

When she was lonely, she and her dog would go into the library where the walls were lined with books and sit by the fire so she could read them stories. The books sat on the looming shelves without any decipherable order. They were not grouped alphabetically or by size, color, or content. Their words brought her peace and contentment, but like her, they were closer to chaos than order. Just like her, the books were left in the castle by a person unknown, without any form of explanation or apology. At night, by the warmth of the fire, the voices of the stories made her and her dog almost feel surrounded by something other than silent space and each other.

She did not know how time passed, but she knew for certain that she had been a little girl once and was now something older. The bed eventually seemed to shrink under her, and she no longer had to climb onto the kitchen counters to open the cabinets. She felt certain that if she had a family surrounding her, they would have taken hundreds of pictures to document and remember the change. She had found an old camera and set it up on a tripod to take care of the task herself. The result was one room lined with the portraits she had taken. The change was slow but clear. If she squinted and ran along the long wall it was almost like watching herself grow in a video, her face changing with whatever mood she had been in as she dutifully took each photograph. Documenting herself for her own enjoyment, she smiled at herself through the lens, imagining there was someone else around to smile back.

One day, while eating lunch, she heard a knock at the door. It was the first time something had made a noise besides her or the dog, so she took a moment to sit in silent confusion before racing her dog to the door. When the knock sounded again, she savored the anticipation, thinking that she was unlikely to have another chance at the experience. Throwing the door open, she found a young man smiling at her with interest. He was taller than her, but she felt an instant recognition that his age must be close to her own. He told her his name, and when she could not respond with her own, he gave her one. When she had no history to answer his story of where he came from, he happily gave her one of those too. He came in and stayed.

Slowly, her once constant routine was altered. For the first time, chores were occasionally forgotten or replaced as he joined his life with hers. They created her past with words and changed her present with laughter and love. He moved out of the empty room he had originally taken and into hers. Watching him age, she knew she was doing the same.

The castle and land around them seemed to shrink with the sounds of their life together, just as her size had shrunk the amount of excess space around her in her bed. His voice joined hers in the library, providing a cast of characters to bring new life to her favorite stories. His silhouette joined hers, black shadows dancing on the massive walls around them conducted by the light of the fire.

One day she woke to find him gone. If it had not been for the slight changes—his face in her once solitary photographs, notes and drawings they had made each other, a name to call the dog—she would have thought he was just a vivid dream. He could have been nothing more than the result of a late night snack of tomatoes.

Eventually she was able to find a new life that blended the two women she had been with and without him. He left her something new and exciting that she had never imagined owning. He gave her a past full of memories of days that did not blend together in a pool of monotony. He gave her a way to mark time, to prove that it had existed.

She often wondered if he would return or if someone else would arrive in his place. Just as she had come to realize when she had stopped being a young girl, she realized she was no longer young at all.

Having felt the joy of human company, his absence left a feeling of loneliness that seemed to carve out whole pieces of her heart. His companionship had made her forget how to do simple chores on her own without his assistance or the content hum of his voice as he chattered next to her. She found herself having to relearn the rules of surviving a life lived alone.

He never returned. No one ever knocked on her door again. Though she had done it occasionally to try to imagine what it had been like for him. Just to stand where he had stood and to feel the hard wood under her hands as he had.

One morning she did not wake. Weeds invaded the soil around her plants, and dust collected on the surface of her books. Though she did not leave her bed, her dog never left her side. If she had ever discovered a reason for her existence, it had been whispered to her dog in the corner of the library. A secret used by the two of them to stay warm as they huddled together fighting off the dark loneliness. Long forgotten.

WHAT DOES IT MEAN TO BE A GROWN-UP?

"'I could tell you my adventures—beginning from this morning' said Alice a little timidly: 'but it's no use going back to yesterday, because I was a different person then.'"

—*Lewis Carroll, Alice's Adventures in Wonderland*

DATA!

Every second, four babies are born and two people die.

"Being a grown-up means chocolate cake for breakfast. I'm sure there are other things, but this one seems to be the most important."

—*Rachel Reiner, 25, mother*

THE HERO WITH A THOUSAND FIXTURES

BY MOBUTU SESE SEKO

My friends and I have all bought houses and developed joint pain. This accounts for perhaps 50 percent of our conversation, the other 50 percent being devoted to people and things we used to do before we developed joint pain or built enough equity in a house to regret losing it to pre–joint pain activities, like adultery. Some of us have even had children, which in the women accounts for the joint pain and in the men accounts for the nostalgia for having sex with someone.

These, then, are the trappings of age, of having "made" it in some baseline way that signifies character progression to others. In the ultimate meatspace role-playing game, we have accrued the essential sword, armor, and stupid guidebook necessary to play the story satisfactorily out to the end. That the first analogy that comes to mind is one related to video games tells you everything you need to know about how essentially unreal the exercise, and thus everything about allegedly being "a grown-up," feels.

I've never read Joseph Campbell, but I've watched *Star Wars* an awful lot. What I've gleaned from the experience—apart from a detailed understanding of what's wrong with George Lucas—is that the arc of a hero's life requires some test of him as a callow youth that, when passed, ushers him into adulthood. Think of Prince Hal, who may or may not be *Star Wars* canon, escaping his debauched languor with Falstaff and taking up arms for England. Agincourt punched his Man Ticket.

My generation lacks such an easy example, but I think the easy example is probably wrong. I've known some peers to lament the absence of a WWII to transmute boyhood into adulthood and forge a new legion of Unquestioned Self-Possessed grown-upness amongst my age group, but they've missed the point entirely. There's a reason why the draft targets people 18–25, and that's because the best way to kill people is to assemble killers with no conception of death. Awareness of mortality creates cowards and questioners and destabilizes unit cohesion.

In this case, adulthood is impossible to achieve if the mechanism for graduating into it necessitates your obliviousness to it. Granted, war's horror produces some actual grown-ups, but it also produces mad men, failures, stagnation, and indifference. Thus its success rate in fostering adulthood hovers somewhere around college's, which is already abysmal.

Frankly, the only institution that I've noticed effectively commands something like adulthood from its members is Home Depot.

What Is Home Depot?

Home Depot is an American big-box store that a parent took you to as a kid while they tried to find the right kind of T-shaped threaded piping that would fix your broken sprinkler system. While they searched for it or a sales clerk, you probably spent time peering through boxes on shelves looking for the largest screw they sold because, hey: big screw. This was the kind of thing people used to assemble bridges or playground structures or other cool big stuff that required screws way bigger than any toy you impatiently watched Dad or Mom assemble on Christmas morning. Later, as you got older, you picked through these boxes because, hey, uhhhh huh-huh-huh-huh, "big screw." Also, you laughed inwardly at "big nuts."

Why Is Home Depot a Test of Adulthood?

First, it meets the requirement, at least in America, of universality. Drive anywhere amongst the cities or suburbs of this land, and you will find it. At some point, it (or Lowe's) must be confronted to achieve some goal related to a responsible life. By this, I mean that Home Depot's purpose is to repair, restore, or build an object of permanence and importance to you. This can range from an object you care for and have invested in to a home/apartment you either own outright or bear an obligation to fix and keep up in some way.

Home Depot is an arbiter of your commitment to the literal maintenance of your own existence. Crossing its threshold of your own volition instantly admits your pledge to something of permanence, some literal or figurative structure in your life. To avoid it entirely yet purchase, via a trained third party, the same goods it provides admits a surrender to someone else's agency. It doesn't even matter if it's something as inane as screwing a GFCI receptacle into the wall: this is self-actualization-level shit.

Why Isn't Something More Meaningful, Well, More Meaningful?

Consider every other metric of importance in your life. Careers, children, money: these are all things that no one expects much expertise from. As soon as one enters a career track, the reality that everyone else entered it within the same sphere of incompetence becomes inescapable. Many co-workers never exit this sphere. Nothing reifies the concept of "fake it 'til you make it" quite like trying to convert comprehensively unhelpful collegiate learning into the tools for navigating the workplace. Everyone else understands the totality of this lie, which is why it takes no personal evolution to grasp it. If anything, having learned something in college will only be unhelpful. Careers usually offer neither regression nor progression. They are just things that happen, and then checks appear.

Money, then, would seem to be some monumental experience one could summit, but that assumes that money makes sense. If Collateralized Debt Obligations and the entire conduct of Wall Street from 2001 to 2007 didn't disabuse you of this conception, then your contemporaries surely will. Nobody really understands money because it doesn't make terribly much sense to begin with. Any economic system that still involves people trying to peg value to a commodity like yellow rock-snot is something based on collective assumptions of value despite utility. Besides, like everyone else you know, you will just get "an investment guy" to handle your stuff. This guy also went to college and learned things that allegedly meant something, took a job that made no sense, figured out how to make appropriately approving or disapproving sounds in response to work stimuli, then wound up getting checks regularly. He also probably has "an investment guy," because he's too busy pretending to say shit that means anything to you, a person who doesn't know anything anyway.

This leaves children, and none of us understands children. Abraham was listening to someone else; Adam didn't see that Cain business coming; and God was an absentee father. This is cosmic-level misunderstanding, from creation to the present. You will not be different.

More importantly, nobody expects you to be different, apart from people who write the sorts of books that presume to create the first generation in history that can "get" its children. Here's why: expertise in the human animal verges on functional impossibility. You probably can't become an expert neuroscientist and psychologist and grasp the changes in your kids as they occur. Nobody expects this of you. If Dave Barry, stand-up comics, and hundreds of dull novels tell us anything, it's that you will never understand.

Only Home Improvement Can Save You

Once you eliminate the other sweeping concerns of your life, all that's left is the box you live in. And that box is instructive, if for nothing more than the fact that it's still comprehensible to you, your children, and your grandparents. What's powerful and compelling about your life is what you can physically create with it. Stop and think about why Jesus was a carpenter. Either he was that committed to being metaphorical or someone on the script committee was just really thoughtful about his job.

Aside from the development of precision tools and an understanding of engineering, carpentry has remained unchanged for centuries. Electrical wiring, though better crafted and more insulated, is a century-old invention. The same goes for indoor plumbing and indoor air circulation, insulation, mass-produced carpets and wallpaper, standardized windows and doors, you name it. Almost nothing about your home is beyond the ken of a man from 1910. Which is what makes it all the more intimidating when you're hopelessly befuddled by it.

Going to Home Depot is the conceptual/commercial version of the dad who tells you that you get one free swing to try to knock it down. Striding in there, assured that you know what you need and can respond to a clerk with knowledge of your problem and the ways to address it is like Ali standing over the supine Liston, only the latter is every predecessor and challenger to your own actualization.

You can get the job to get the money to fund having the kids, but all those are things any fuckup can do. Your co-workers and bozo millionaires and fat trailer park children bespeak the essential ease with which all those things can happen. All those things can be achieved or managed by something else, concepts and responsibilities deferred, understanding not forthcoming. Having something concrete—or drywall, or stucco, or wood-sided—in your hands and correcting its problems for yourself presents undeniable evidence of your own agency.

It's nothing so grandiose as a Maslowian conception of shelter but rather a grasp of transcendent and timeless knowledge and craft. Crossing the Home Depot threshold demands of you some rudimentary experience with the thing built almost literally around your life. You can stand in the aisle and ask questions, pretend huffily to look for something you expect to find there, but you know when you're faking it. You know what authenticity feels like, and you know the shame you feel without it. Even if you're only tweaking, augmenting, or prettifying something, you know that Home Depot is the test that you have built something, that your life is now your own. And you know how much you want to pass.

DAD WAS NOT A HAPPY ZOMBIE

BY MARCUS GOODYEAR

There's an Uzi in our parlor. That's what Mom called our entryway where her collection of crosses still hangs to welcome visitors. Dad never liked the word "parlor," but he would have liked the gun in the umbrella bin, handle out, so you can grab the butt and be shooting pretty quick if you need to.

My brother makes me practice all the time.

"Faster, Thomas," he'll say, chewing on a toothpick as though we had an endless supply of toothpicks. "There's a mob at the door, ready to break in. You gotta be fast if you wanna mow them down."

I don't. Not really, but we keep a gun in every room because they attack sometimes. An Uzi in the parlor. A shotgun on top of the broken fridge next to the fly swatter. We know the bullets will run out someday, so we have machetes and baseball bats along with the pistols and rifles in the full arsenal in our parents' old room, laid out on their mattress, ready to use.

"But I don't like killing zombies," I told my brother at breakfast. It was my tenth birthday, so we were sharing a can of pears before we went scavenging.

"They want your brains, Tom."

"Not on my birthday," I said.

"Even on your birthday."

The pears were my present, but I wanted a day without killing and I wouldn't let it go.

"When was the last time a zombie ate anyone?" I asked. "They are too slow and too dumb."

"They can still bite you."

"So," I mumbled.

"So, you want to hit puberty and become one of them? I don't."

The strange virus only affected adults. That was why the kids survived and the adults didn't. Only now there weren't many kids left, and we couldn't trust them not to turn one night when their hormones activated the virus or however it worked.

My brother offered me the can full of syrup, which I took and greedily drained, the edge of the can sharp against my lips. Today, I did not have to share.

"They never stop, Thomas, unless we stop them."

"Even on my birthday?"

"We have to be like the pill bugs and the vultures. We do our part to clean death out of the world."

I knew what he meant, but it was still hard to get past knowing them. All the adults in our little town of 20,000 people, now dead and roaming the streets, the old Baptist preacher in his ragged slacks, all our teachers from the school, police officers too dumb to know they can use the guns on their belts, McDonald's workers in soiled uniforms, everyone wearing what they were wearing when the adult plague hit. It had destroyed their minds, then stopped their hearts and left a world full of orphans.

"Just kill them," my brother said. "They don't know it's your birthday, and they can attack us tonight like any other night."

"But they are so slow!" I said. I want what I want for my birthday.

My brother ignored me. "They attack us at night, and we attack them during the day wherever we find them."

So I knew what to do when we were out scavenging, a rifle slung over my shoulder. My brother went inside a house but not before pointing at the zombie on the sidewalk.

"Take care of that one," he said.

It was tangled in kite string, a tattered rainbow kite shaped like a parrot swinging at the creature's waist. As if they weren't slow enough, this one had cocooned itself in the kite and the string and now it was hung up on an old mailbox. It moaned and pulled so that the mailbox clanged back and forth against it, a strange, sharp sound in the silence of our dead town.

I raised the rifle and looked through the scope, planning a clean shot to the head, and even before he turned to face me, before it turned, I recognized the suit coat. His thin hair was dirty with caked blood against his skull so that he looked bald now, but still recognizable: our dad.

I lowered the gun and tried to breathe. Up and down the street, it was just us. The others had wandered into the shade of the green belt probably, or they were waiting inside the houses where the doors were left open.

There weren't enough memories of him, but he had tried to come home for dinner most nights. He would lead the prayer and shovel the food down like a marine on the front lines. But he also had his dinner ritual. We went around the table, each of us, explaining our day to him before he headed back to the store.

He would set his fork down, lean away from the table with his evening coffee and ask, "What have you done today to justify your existence?" He rarely answered the question himself, which I assumed to mean he didn't need to justify anything to anyone.

That's a hard question to answer when you are in the first or second grade. I wanted to play with Legos and run in the yard with the dogs, but none of that seemed to justify anything for me. We had everything. A big house. Big cars. A toy room with more game systems than we knew what to do with, all of them useless now that the electricity was off. We even had a good dad who ate dinner with us nearly every night. On the weekends, he took me with him to the store and let me play in the back room with the boxes. Everything in the store came to us from a box, and Saturday we constructed whole box worlds, mazing up the room with clutter until some zit-faced employee complained to Dad that he couldn't get to the bathroom. Sometimes Dad would really let us have it then, depending on how the day was going. Customers or suppliers yelled at him. He yelled at us. Then we yelled at each other.

I had seen Dad before, shuffling along the asphalt. He came by the house sometimes, but I didn't shoot him then, and I was not going to shoot today. Not on my birthday or any day. I wouldn't do it. Of course, my brother always gave me a hard time about this. Last time Dad came to the house, I had to play some hysterics to get him to leave it alone. In the morning, Dad wandered off, just like they always do.

"We can't be soft like this," my brother said after we let Dad go.

"But we're alive because of him."

My brother scoffed at this. "Any grown man can have sex with some girl and make kids. At least they used to."

We hadn't seen any grown men in a few months. Not since the disease. "He set this up for us. He got the bullets and guns out of the store. He filled the truck and brought it here so we could lie low while everything settled down."

"He left us, Thomas."

"He died for us."

"He put on his suit and gave up."

I couldn't explain the suit, but it wasn't a simple suicide. I stuck to my story. "He died for us."

So far, my story was working, but we were getting more desperate. The truck food had gone quicker than we expected, and we didn't know what we were going to do. The world died and forgot about us in our big house with all the empty aluminum cans.

If I left Dad there, my brother would probably kill him this time. Take my rifle and shoot for the head, rolling his eyes at me. I know they aren't who they were. But I can't help seeing what I see. That's my dad in his suit. How did he get wrapped in a kite like that? It was ridiculous. How did he get tied around the mailbox? He wasn't dangerous. I walked closer, annoyed by the moaning and his teeth clacking at me like I should roll over and let him eat me for lunch in broad daylight. Or at least bite me. There was no justifying existence anymore except to kill or be killed. They didn't like the light either, so Dad was not a happy zombie. He wanted shade, some corner to hide until dusk came again. I could give him that for my birthday. Let him be, let him live or move or whatever we call this new kind of life that people have after life. Exist.

I walked toward him slowly, confident but cautious, and pulled the hunting knife from my belt. Another treasure from the store that Dad got before the looters. Of course, we got all their treasures anyway when they were overrun at the various bunker communities they built. Not us. Dad told us to keep to ourselves, simplify, simplify, simplify. Like my brother always said. Don't use an Uzi if you have a pistol. Don't use a pistol if you have an axe. Don't use an axe or a bat or anything at all if you can just lie low and let the problem shuffle away on its own. That last rule was mine, not my brother's.

Dad wasn't doing well. The suit was tattered. He had lost his hands somehow, so that one was just a bony wrist with blackened muscle and flaps of skin poking out of his sleeve when he reached for me. The other arm was much shorter and the sleeve swung empty, hiding the piece of arm or elbow or shoulder inside. Our family never cared for hugs.

I circled him a few times, watching the house where my brother was looking for goods. There wasn't much left to pick over these days, so he could be gone awhile if he explored every cabinet, closet, and drawer, looking for things others might have missed.

"How are you doing today, Dad?" I asked him.

He pulled against the mailbox, and it squeaked in its concrete base.

"What have you done today to justify your existence?" I asked.

Dad's teeth bit the air.

He didn't smell good at all. I forget how bad they smell up close. The whole town has this cloud of stink now, but when you get close you remember where the stink comes from. My brother has this dream of killing them all one day. We can rebuild the town ourselves. That's his dream. Tear down some backyard fences and set up a farm. Or else we could walk to one of the hay farms outside of town. There was probably grain waiting to be picked out there right now. Grain could make bread.

I thought rabbits might work, too, but my brother said rabbits weren't efficient. And they would attract the dead. We used to have deer all over the place in our small town. Dad would yell at them when they ate whatever he planted. "Yard rats," he called them. We don't have that problem anymore.

Honestly, though, I get tired of eating the roaches. I could see some of them inside Dad's coat. We weren't sure if the bugs were eating the dead or not. They seemed to be doing a slow job of it if they were.

Looking closer at Dad on the mailbox, I realized this was going to be impossible. There was no way I could untangle that mess. I was never good with tangled up fishing poles either, so I would do with Dad what I did with the fishing poles, cut the line completely and start over.

Not that I would set Dad free. Even a slow zombie with no hands can surprise you sometimes. No. First, I cut the kite string free at the spool. Then I tied it onto Dad's ankle, down low where he couldn't reach me since he was all tangled and connected to the mailbox. He grunted and moaned at me and shook the thin pole, but zombies just aren't very strong.

What they are is persistent.

I'm not sure what I had in mind exactly when I cut Dad free from the mailbox. I expected him to lead me down the street like a dog on a leash. Or maybe I would lead him, and we would go for a stroll, the rifle over my shoulder, the little string in my right hand.

I was whistling "Happy Birthday" to myself when Dad turned and kicked me over. It wasn't a strong kick so much as surprising, and I toppled over from my crouch. Then Dad fell on me, clacking his jaw and waving his arm stumps.

My brother came out of the house in time to see my plan fall apart.

I scrambled away quick, but not before Dad bit into my side. Like the kick, it wasn't a particularly effective bite. It would heal within a week if I took care of it. But such bites are persistent. In a few more birthdays, the virus would explode within me.

"Thomas!" my brother yelled. He ran to me and fired on Dad nearly point blank. The noise was so loud. "Thomas, you're bit," he said.

"Don't worry," I told him. I had plenty of birthdays left before I would grow up.

Dad twitched, and my brother fired again. So loud.

WHAT DOES IT MEAN TO BE A GROWN-UP?

"Ownership of the following items: a box of envelopes, Neosporin, rolls of tape (at least Scotch, masking, duct, also painters, packing, athletic, and electrical if you've really made it), tax preparation software, napkins, and spare keys."

—*Allison, 25, working on it*

"It's that first time someone looks at you and asks, 'What do we need to do?'

The magic of being a grown-up is like the magic of Santa Claus. I know it's fake, but the kids don't, and they won't know until they have to be grown-ups themselves."

—*Scott Cockrell, 43, Taoist*

DATA!

On average, Americans spend 2.7 hours per day, or 11.25 percent of their lives, watching TV.

DATA!

Average age of the US population: 36.8 years

NO CHOICE

BY SAM POW

Dr. Bagley said I grew up fast because I had to, but that's bullshit. She's the psychiatrist that comes here on Wednesdays. Having your childhood tooken from you and being grown up are two different things. The fact that I knew about sex and drugs when I was a little kid doesn't make me mature for my age. I learned how to boost clothes from Ross and food from the market when I was like ten. I took care of my little brother and sister, changed them, cooked for them, starting when I was like eight. Is that growing up? Nah. I say it ain't.

Mr. Hall, he my therapist, he said we learn from our parents no matter what. Sometimes they might teach us what to do or how to act, other times they might teach us what not to do. He's always asking how I can look at a situation as an opportunity for growth. Ugh! "Opportunity for growth!" That's like his favorite words. Ha!

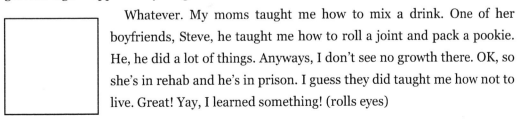 Whatever. My moms taught me how to mix a drink. One of her boyfriends, Steve, he taught me how to roll a joint and pack a pookie. He, he did a lot of things. Anyways, I don't see no growth there. OK, so she's in rehab and he's in prison. I guess they did taught me how not to live. Great! Yay, I learned something! (rolls eyes)

I guess I look grown up, like a woman. I've had this booty and these titties, ha-ha, since I was 'bout twelve, that's over four years already. I don't feel no different though. Yeah. I guess people do treat me different though. They sure look at me different. Shi-it. An I can use it. Ya know? Flirt a lil' bit to git what I want. Is that grown-up? I don't know.

Mr. Mike, he's one of the CCCs (Child Care Counselors) here, he asked me if I was grown up enough to keep a secret. I said yes. Maybe I shouldn't of. Then he kissed me. We have sex in the laundry room sometimes. It's cool. He smiles at me sometimes during his shift. I like it. Sometimes he bring me Red Vines from the liquor store. I love Red Vines. I like to use them as a straw for a bottle of Coke. I started doing that when I would go to the movie matinee's sometimes on Saturday's with Mrs. Ward and her two little boys. She was my second foster mom, back when I was thirteen. Her name was Shelly. Shelly Ward. Anyways, we would get a big cup of Coke that had refills, and we would share it. We'd have to make the hole in the top bigger so we could fit a Red Vine straw for each of us in it.

I miss Mrs. Ward. That was my best placement, by far, but I fucked it up just like all the other ones. Mr. Ward liked to yell at me, um, about peeing on the mattress. (sigh) Oh god, this is embarrassing. OK. The peeing started when I was eleven or twelve. Back then, Steve would wake me up almost every night, really, really late, when he would get up from being passed out on the couch. I could bet that I would wake up with him touching me. If I had peed in my sleep he would touch me with his fists. That was almost better than when I would wake up with him touching me with his hands or his mouth, or, other things.

Dr. Bagley says I have something called insomnia. That's why she gives me Trazodone. I'm able to sleep better now, but I still piss myself in the night sometimes. Most of the counselor's don't get too mad about it. They learned real quick to use a plastic mattress cover thingy on my bed.

So yeah, Mr. Ward got pretty bent about me and the bed wetting. At first I would just apologize a lot and cry a little bit, but Mr. Ward, he wouldn't let it go. He started saying that if I was really sorry, I wouldn't do it no more. He started sayin' shit like, "We took you in here and this is what we get? C'mon! Show some respect." He was always saying c'mon this or c'mon that, blah, blah blah. He even started talkin' smack if I drank any water before bed.

One morning when I was trying to pull the wet sheets off my bed real quick before he noticed, Mr. Ward came in and told me he was done. I had been with the Ward family for over six months and Mrs. Ward told me that they were hoping to adopt me and that they had filled out some paperwork to get that whole thing started. Anyways, that morning Mr. Ward said he was done with me and my ungrateful attitude and lack of respect for him and his house. He said I was gross. I stood there looking at the bed, crying, with my hands turning into fists holding the balled up sheets. I couldn't say I was sorry anymore. Now, Mr. Hall has taught me how to take a deep breath and count backward from five when I'm really mad, so that I don't say something stupid, but back then I didn't know about that. I told Mr. Ward, "Well fuck you then, Dick Face!" or something like that. Then I threw the sheets at him. His jaw dropped and his face turned dark red. I ran out the room and he called me a little bitch. I threw myself onto the couch and saw their son Zack standing in the hallway. It looked like he was crying. He was seven. I squished my face into the cushion, screamin' and ballin' cuz I knew what was gonna happen. Then Mr. and Mrs. Ward started arguing about canceling the adoption and I couldn't take it. I ran into the room and grabbed my shoes and then walked to school without eating breakfast or fixing my hair or anything.

At lunch some 8th grade bitch called me ghetto cuz I was just wearing a thermal undershirt and my hair was messed up. I spit at her and got sent to the office. On the way home from school, I felt sick. I didn't want to go to the house. I bought some hairspray and huffed that shit behind the dumpster in back of Rite Aid. I guess I was acting funny when I went to the house cuz Mr. Ward started yelling, "Great, she's on drugs. I told you she was on drugs!" He searched through my whole room. I didn't have any drugs, but he did find the little razor blade I had tooken out of my old leg shaver. I guess there was a little blood on it or something cuz he said, "Roll up your sleeves." My heart stopped. I didn't feel foggy no more. "NOW! Roll up your sleeves right now!" He grabbed my arm and pushed my sleeve up. "Oh my God!" He made a nasty face and threw my arm down.

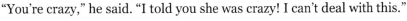

"You're crazy," he said. "I told you she was crazy! I can't deal with this."

I ran away that night. I didn't even think about it. I had to. No way was I gonna deal with more of Mr. Ward's bullshit in the morning and just wait around for DCFS to take me away again. I didn't even say goodbye to Mrs. Ward or the kids. Fuck... I went to my Mom's neighborhood where the street people knew me and I could hustle myself and stay high. Then I went to the Youth Authority Camp for a while, a couple group homes, another foster home and now here at Oak Grove Group Home.

Mr. Hall says there's a difference between reacting and responding. He says when you react, it's like someone pushes a button and you just react to it automatic. When you respond, you think first, then decide what to do. Mr. Hall said, "You choose how to handle the bullshit instead of letting the bullshit handle you." Mr. Hall is crazy like that but his shit does make sense though. He's always talking about choices and consequences. He said that in a year and a half I'm a be an adult, so I have to start thinking about the choices I want to make and what the consequences of those choices might be.

I still react though. It was really hard when Erica was here. She was seventeen, 5' 10" and always wore lip gloss and tight ass jeans. Mr. Mike looked at her like he would always look at me. Everybody thought Erica was all that cuz she told a lot of stories about crazy shit she did when she had her sugar daddy and all the drugs she wanted and all the sex parties. She also had tattoos but not the homemade juvie kind that most of us have. She had some skulls and naked girls and flowers and stuff and that shit was quality. Erica also told everyone that she was gay for the stay so a lot of the girls were tryin' to holler at her and would do whatever she told them to. When Mr. Mike and the other guy counselors were around, she would always be twirling her hair and leaning over a lot to show her cleavages with this crooked little smile. That bitch was scandalous, but everyone seemed to think she was the business, even Mr. Mike. He stopped payin' me much attention, and a couple of the girls told me they heard Erica talkin' 'bout suckin' his dick in the supply closet. Erica AWOLed a few days later. The girls say they saw a guy pull up in some car, and she just ran out and got in it with her bags packed and everything.

Anyways, one night when Erica was still here, Mr. Mike told me I had to redo my chore and I went off on him. I called him a dumb fucker or some shit like that. That got my behavior level dropped to "C", so I didn't get to go on rec. to the beach that weekend. I never been to the beach. They say it's only like thirty minutes from here, but I never been to the beach.

I hope when I'm grown up I can choose to go to the beach. It's just, the girls I know that aged out of the system, the foster system or whatever, they all either on the street slangin' dope er somethin' or gots a sugar daddy or something like that. Or, they moved back in with they moms er somethin', but I ain't tryin' to do none a that.

No, that's not true. Claudia, she gots a job at McDonald's, and she got a low income housing. She always bitching about her boss and the grease and the roaches in her apartment, but she did it. The counselors use her as an example. They say "Claudia, she transitioned out of Oak Grove successfully."

Is that what being a successful adult is? Claudia didn't get to choose her apartment, her case manager from Oak Grove helped her get it. Claudia doesn't get to choose her work schedule and the job sucks, but who else would hire her? I don't even have my GED like she does, and I have like a hunded twenty units left for me to graduate. I'll prolly be like twenty before I get my diploma.

How am I gonna "respond" like an adult when I turn eighteen and they put me outa here? I'm prolly gonna "react" and go survive like I know how to. Mr. Hall would say I have a choice. I say my choices are all different shades of shit. Haha... Fuck. I don't know. I need to take a deep breath.

MY DAD THE GHOST RIDER

BY ZACK PARSONS

The first time my face turned into the grim rictus mask of a fleshless skull was also my first kiss. The lucky boy was Brad Dillford, and it was the beginning of summer following an arduous sixth grade. I rode my bike to the park that day, and by coincidence or fate I found Brad Dillford throwing rocks at the light above the dugout at the baseball diamond.

Brad tortured me throughout fifth and sixth grade. I don't mean that childish confusion of lust and aggression that ends up in girls getting their hair pulled or their shoes kicked under the table. Brad pushed me down in puddles, threw juice in my hair, tore up my favorite folder, and wrote "you love gary klutcha" on my arm in permanent marker. I definitely did not love Gary Kleczka, who bit our math teacher and I think had Down's Syndrome.

Brad had pet names for me like "Mere-breath" and "Smelly M" and "Fat Meredith," which was not clever at all and at least partly responsible for my struggle with my weight throughout high school and college.

The single meanest thing he did to me was the time he "found" my missing lunch bag and then stared at me while I ate everything. When I finished, he told me that he had taken it all out and farted on it in the bathroom.

"So you'd get skinny," he claimed.

I ate a chicken salad and Brad Dillford fart sandwich. Makes it kind of hard to explain how I got from wanting to poke out his eyes with pencils to smooching him in the picnic pavilion at Castle Family Memorial Park.

He said, "Bet you won't kiss me." That was it. That was his line.

I guess sometimes you hate something so much you start to love it. When our lips touched it was like a wet, Frito-flavored door to the future opening.

I think we were both a little amazed. The passion was there. I realized I could love this boy, even if it was for all the wrong reasons. That's about when my face's skin and muscle melted off and my head turned into a skull. Brad Dillford ran screaming right into the oil drum trash can with all the yellow jackets buzzing around it.

"What's wrong?" I asked. I didn't know that my head was a skull. I thought I might have kissed him so badly it made him run screaming.

It wasn't until I saw myself reflected in the chrome spit-guard of the park's drinking fountain that I realized why Brad was running. This wasn't just cheekbones poking through when I looked in my compact. Not another noseless face when I climbed out of the shower and wiped away the steam. I'd gone full-on skull for the first time and it happened seconds after my first kiss.

Yeah, that will mess with a girl's self-image. I changed back after only a few seconds, but the damage was done. I ran all the way home and left my bike at the park. I locked myself in the bathroom—much to the chagrin of my sisters Diana and Madison—and sobbed my way through a whole box of tissues. When Dad got home he had to pry the story out of me through the bathroom door. He listened patiently, but when I told him I left my bike at the park, he finally said something.

"You can't ditch your bike, baby. You're a Ghost Rider!"

To be clear, my father wasn't *the* Ghost Rider, not the one most people know about, but he was *a* Ghost Rider. But not me. I refused to accept that life.

"No I'm not!" I sobbed through the bathroom door. "I'll never be a Ghost Rider. I hate them. I hate you for selling my soul to the devil!"

"It was the souls of all of my children, not just you, and he tricked me. And it technically wasn't the devil. It was a lesser, but still-powerful, demon."

That just made me angrier. I screamed at Dad to go away and covered my ears.

When I finally came out of the bathroom, my bike was in the hallway, and Mom and Dad were waiting for me at the kitchen table with a leftover plate of mac and cheese with hot dog buttons (my favorite at that age). They had a long talk with me about being a Ghost Rider. I'd heard variations on that talk since first grade. Dad was always warning me about projecting hellfire when I got angry, or summoning a spectral motorcycle, but that stuff never happened. The skull was the first sign I might take after Dad, and my two sisters and I were furious.

"If you embrace it, you can learn to control it," said Dad.

"It can be tough, but your destiny is to be a Ghost Rider," said Mom.

What did she know? She wasn't even a Ghost Rider, she was just a regular woman that Dad rescued from hell after fighting a dragon made out of metal. Mom could never understand my pain.

THIS IMAGE IS BLURRED DUE TO BEING SUPER COPY-RIGHTED AND MEGA PROTECTED BY LAW

"Diana has a boyfriend, and Madison is in cheerleading," said Dad. "You can lead a normal life, you just need to be prepared and make time for your Ghost Riding. When the change comes you'll be a great—"

I couldn't bear another word. I ran upstairs to my room and slammed the door and threw myself into the understanding embrace of my stuffed animals. Tears rolled down fleshless cheeks. I had changed back to the skull again.

That afternoon with Brad was the first time my heritage intruded on my attempts to be a normal girl, but it would not be the last. For what remained of my childhood, I fought an increasingly desperate battle to deny being a Ghost Rider.

I could fill a book with all the times I was embarrassed or humiliated by my uncontrolled transformations. There was prom night, when my dress changed into a leather jacket covered in spikes. There was the time I was flirting with Mr. Samuelson, the cute English teacher, and my libido somehow conjured a burning motorcycle to crash through the door and cast the entire classroom in the unearthly glow of its hellfire. I had to schedule my senior pictures like ten times because I kept having skull breakouts. Cramming for tests was hard because of all the dreams I'd have about being a bride of Zarathos, this creepy giant green skeleton entity Dad sold our souls to so he could save Mom.

The Ghost Rider thing even messed my life up when it wasn't manifesting. I remember my first time in college with this guy, Lloyd. I spent our entire date at Crab Lobster touching my face over and over again to make sure everything was OK. When we finally did it in my dorm, I couldn't enjoy myself because I was so worried my head would turn into a skull. I bet he thought I was kinky asking him to cover my face with a pillow every time we had sex. It took eight weeks of dating before I showed my face in bed. Then we got in a fight over his MMO gaming, and I projected a stream of hellfire into his computer.

That was it for me and Lloyd. You can't really continue with a relationship after you've used your powers in anger. As Batman famously said in those PSAs, "No matter how sorry you are, you can't take back a Batarang."

Mom and Dad didn't help. Mom would leave these passive aggressive notes telling me, "Madison is overmatched against Sky Hitler. I really hope she doesn't get hurt battling his Terror Copters," or wondering, "Have you thought what you would do if your father and I were decapitated by Brass Genie?"

Dad, on the other hand, was relentless. He bought me leather jackets every year for Christmas and my birthday, and any time he heard me complain about something he asked me if I had considered seeking supernatural vengeance. If I had a mean biology TA, failed a math exam, or just had a lunch served colder than I liked, Dad would bring up the vengeance thing. I felt like I could barely talk to either of them.

Dad was also aggressively involved in my love life. He pressured me to settle down with every boy I dated for more than a week, and not because he wanted me in a stable relationship. Oh, no, Dad wanted me to be so deeply in love that when one of his underworld pals killed my boyfriend and spread his guts all over my dorm or my apartment, I would have no choice but to devote my life to seeking vengeance. I think he was joking when he would threaten that stuff.

When I wasn't dating somebody it was worse. There was always a new villain Dad wanted to introduce me to with some elaborate story of misdeeds.

There was Cyber Pedro, the Alternate Hulk, some snake man named Danny, and an escaped hell demon that he referred to as Esteban the Bloody. He thought for sure I could date them and then need to hunt them down and send them to hell for being sleazebags. Sometimes he came at me with these stories I hardly even believed.

"Cob King," he said. "You remember that trip to Iowa when you were a little girl? I had to send Corn Lord back to the Third Circle. Well, Cob King was his son and he is taking over his father's high-fructose empire. They're working with the Pennsylvania Techno-Amish to turn America's inner-city kids into gluttonous fructose thralls. You'll love him."

"Tell Diana about it." My stock response was always to pawn these guys off on my sisters, who he had already convinced into the life of Ghost Riding.

I was in college finishing my master's degree in veterinary medicine when Dad died. It came as a shock to everyone. It didn't seem possible. He'd been to hell so many times. Time travel, the moon, weird military bases, none of it really phased him. We were complacent I guess. Nobody even noticed the symptoms. Defeated by the greatest foe he'd ever faced: hypertension. How could a burning skull have a stroke? It didn't make biological sense. The doctor said he was driving up the side of a building when it happened, chasing after a corrupt politician who'd made his own bargain with the devil.

"If the stroke hadn't killed him, the fall would have been fatal," said the doctor.

"No," Mom said. "He once fell ten miles into the burning abyss. He is invulnerable to falls."

Diana, always closest to Dad, was inconsolable. She was working as a Ghost Rider in Detroit and had to take the bus. She couldn't even stand to look at her motorcycle from hell, let alone conjure it. Madison left all these tearful phone messages, but she always avoids problems and so she never came. Not even to the funeral.

"I'm so sorry," Madison sobbed into the phone, "but a mutant super soldier has been killing prostitutes in Newark. These women need me to avenge them."

I couldn't blame her. She was always more comfortable with the act of being a Ghost Rider than living as one. I was struggling with the reality of Dad's death too. I remembered all those times I'd been mean to him. I became obsessed with the idea that the last time I talked to him I hung up the phone without saying goodbye. I imagined him hanging up that stupid football phone of his and sitting in his darkened garage, skull burning the blue-green it got when he forgot to take his antidepressants, wondering where he'd gone wrong with me. Wondering why I rejected him so totally.

Those days after Dad died are hazy, but I clearly recall Mom's strength. She made the funeral arrangements, and each of us had our turn crying on her shoulder. That day at the viewing, I don't think I saw her shed a single tear. He was in the casket looking like a normal man. Looking more alive than he had in years.

Dad's weird superhero friends were all there. I knew some of their normal alter-egos, but they showed up in full regalia. Even some of the villains he'd defeated. There was this guy that was like a giant head in a mechanical suit. He thanked Mom and said that if it weren't for Dad he'd still be designing robots to kill people, but now he designs robots to help the elderly and rescue people from fires.

Watching Mom stoically greet all these people and accept their condolences, I realized she was as amazing as Dad. Even if her head didn't turn into a skull or burst into flames, even if she couldn't summon a spectral motorcycle with the raw power of vengeance, she was still a hero.

I helped her clean up the house after the wake cleared out. There was so much terrible food to wrap up and put away. Lots of birthday cake type stuff. Superheroes almost never die, and, even when they do, they tend to come back from the dead, so they don't know how to handle a wake. When it was finally done, we sat together in the kitchen and had a beer. Dad's terrible domestics with the picture of the winged skull and BEER spelled out on the label.

"He was proud of you," said Mom.

"I know."

"No, you don't. He could never tell you, but he was proud that you weren't a Ghost Rider. He understood how hard it was to deal with the flaming skull and all the rest of it while trying to put yourself through college to be a veterinarian. He really respected that."

"How could he know what it was like?"

"Oh, he knew what it was like. He had his hippie phase he went through where he was going to change the world. Lasted all of about a week before he got mad at some Nixon flunky and destroyed his car with hellfire. But he couldn't hack it. Not like you've managed. He always gave into that stuff and there's nothing wrong with it, but he knew there could have been so much more to life than just driving up the side of a cliff to kill a devil centipede.

"Like spaying and neutering pets," Mom said. "Follow that dream, for him."

It took an extra year because of that incident with the mummy I won't go into here, it's all over the Internet, but I finally graduated from college with my degree. Helping animals was all that mattered to me. I joined one of those vet clinics that work out of a pet-food chain. Paid the bills and I got to work with animals. Something still wasn't right though, I could feel it. I was still having those dreams about the demonic being that owns my soul, and I'd wake up with full burning skull head.

I tried throwing myself into my work, but I only found myself getting more distracted by sudden skull shifts and unintentional hellfire projections. Trust me, when you've got an iguana named Pedro open on the table so you can cut the dimes he swallowed out of his gut the last thing you need is a burning motorcycle crashing through the operating room doors.

That was when the puppy mill incident happened. We run into them occasionally. Animal control finds an unlicensed breeder with inhumane dog kennels, and they round up all the animals. We have an open door on that sort of thing and run weekend adoptions to help the ASPCA. This one was real bad. A world-class sleazebag named Tad Snivelwhip was running a puppy mill practically like a chicken farm. There were dogs dead in cages with live dogs, starvation, overheating, lack of water, and physical abuse. The guy got out of jail on a technicality.

When I read Snivelwhip bragging in the paper how he was going to do it again, I snapped. I threw the newspaper down in disgust and at that moment, in the Pets Planet break room, I realized my destiny. I allowed all of my anger about the mistreatment of animals to flow into my body. I felt so powerful. My skull started burning, my vet coat turned into a black leather jacket covered in spikes, and a flaming motorcycle burst through the break-room door, overturning the table and spilling Kathy's bento box.

"I have Dairy King gift certs I can give you to replace that!" I shouted as I revved my mystical motorcycle and zoomed out of the Pets Planet. All of the dogs receiving shampooing watched me roar past the Pampered Pet Grooming Center. I think I saw, in the black jellybeans of their eyes, a triumphant "Hell yeah!" and maybe a little "You go, girl!"

I had to kill my way through Snivelwhip's henchmen. Lots of guidos yelling "yo" and shooting Uzis at me. There was a foreman with white hair and an eyepatch who fought me with a katana sword and could disappear into shadows, but I grabbed him with a chain and dragged him up to the ceiling on my motorcycle. First time I ever choked a man to death.

Snivelwhip was waiting for me in the condemned warehouse he was planning to turn into the state's second-largest puppy mill. I scared his Ukrainian stripper nymphs away with a rev of my spectral engine and vaulted up the marble staircase to his luxurious office. He had an M-16 with a grenade launcher in his hands and stacked bottles of Shiba Inu semen on ice.

"I can inseminate a mutt and get a purebred," he bragged, fingering the Dewar flasks of frozen gold. He paraded around the desk and brandished his assault rifle. "I'll clear over $3,000 a month. My plan is foolproof, but it only works if you're gone. Sorry, it's time for you to go back to hell."

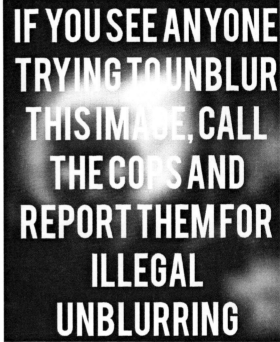

Really? That was my first Ghost Riding and even I knew an assault rifle was harmless. I let him shoot a full magazine into me and then I opened a tunnel to hell.

"Please, don't!" he begged. "I have a family! Cruelty to animals isn't even a sin! You can't do this!"

"I'm a Ghost Rider," I said. "I can do anything I want."

It felt good throwing Snivelwhip into the abyss. As the demonic sphincter was closing, I think I heard Dad, his distant voice echoing up from Satan's bowel, shouting, "I love you, Meredith!"

I'm not afraid of what I am anymore. I'm not running from it. I've managed to find a way to live my life: be a veterinarian, have a healthy relationship, and Ghost Ride on my terms. It may not be the traditional way of a Ghost Rider. I may not fight the usual sort of villain, but I know I'm making my father proud.

Someday, after I am finally defeated by breast cancer or diabetes, when I am being flensed by Zarathos in the depths of his horror pits, I'll tell my father the truth: I was always proud of my Ghost Rider Dad.

WHAT DOES IT MEAN TO BE A GROWN-UP?

"Finally all the mail is for you...alas, it's all bills."

—*Amy, 35, music teacher, horrible housekeeper*

DATA!

Percentage of men 25–34 in US living with parents:

14 in 2005

19 in 2011

DATA!

Average age of Nobel Prize winner: 63

"And thanks be to God, Johnny, said Mr Dedalus, that we lived so long and did so little harm."

—*James Joyce*, A Portrait of the Artist as a Young Man

DRIVER

BY MEG BASHWINER

I was sixteen when we launched a 1984 Volvo wagon five feet into the air. My friend Lindsay was driving, I sat shotgun, and Mike was in the back. Ben Folds was playing on the radio, or maybe it was the soundtrack to *Chicago*. Considering the times and the company, it had to have been one or the other. For the purposes of this story, let's say it was both. Ben and Roxie Hart wailed away while we flew.

There's this road in Little Falls, New Jersey, that is equidistant from the best dinner ever and my house. It was traveled often by Lindsay's 1984 Volvo wagon, lovingly named Doris. The road is a steep hill that levels out on a set of railroad tracks, immediately followed by an even steeper incline.

It had been observed that if you started at the top of the hill and got the car to about forty miles per hour by the time you hit the railroad tracks, you would launch several feet in the air, landing a few seconds later. Good clean fun. We did this often.

This particular time there was a glint in Lindsay's eye as she accelerated to seventy miles per hour, the fastest Doris had ever gone in her eighteen years of rust-ridden existence. When we hit the tracks, we were no longer in a car, but an airplane, an airplane that would make the Wright Brothers stand back in awe. We were in the air for what must have been hours, long enough for the earth to rotate beneath us and push us even farther. Babies were born, casseroles were made, houses were built, and marriages ended, all while we flew through the air. And then we landed.

Boom.

The sound of Mike's scrawny fifteen-year-old body hitting the ceiling of the car.

Screeeech.

The sound of the tires welcoming themselves back to the unfamiliar feeling of solid ground.

_____.

The sound of silence as our teenage bodies realized what we had just done.

"Are you OK, dude?" one of us probably said to Mike. "Yeah, man," he probably said back, because when you're fifteen, your body is hard to fuck up, and a flight across train tracks and the subsequent smack of your body onto a metal car ceiling is nothing, nothing but a story that we could tell our friends when we got back. Nothing but a story.

That's all that there is when you're a sixteen-year-old kid in suburbia: shitty cars with funny names, diners, aimlessly driving around doing stupid kid shit, and living to tell the tale. To be fair, that's all that you need. Add a couple packs of cigarettes and whatever booze you can sneak from your parents' liquor cabinet and you've got it made. Ben Folds would probably agree. Roxie Hart could not be reached for comment.

When I got my license at seventeen, and Lindsay went off to college, it was my time to be the driver. I was given a 1986 Jeep Cherokee in champagne (baby shit) gold. My parents got the car for free from a co-worker. I named the Jeep Bea Arthur because she was old and gold. Bea and I were in this thing, this "driving" thing, together, and I was petrified. Maybe it was all the flying around we had done in Lindsay's car, or that fact that I have never been the most attentive or coordinated person, or that my driving instructor yelled at me a lot in between pulls of Pall Malls. I was freaked out.

When, having gotten my learner's permit, my sister tried to teach me how to drive a manual in a parking lot the size of this comma, we came millimeters from crashing her green 1996 Jetta into a brick wall. She pulled the emergency brake; we screeched to a halt, and she made me walk home in anxiety-ridden anguish. I have yet to live this down, almost ten years later.

To say I was a nervous driver is an understatement. I gripped the wheel with white knuckles, my foot shook on the brake, and sweat rolled down my spine. Bea overheated, her ceiling leaked, her heat was broken, she got stuck in four-wheel drive a lot, and the left blinker never canceled. We were perfect for each other, each a complete fucking mess. With me behind the wheel, and her being the wheel, we drove onward together, horrified of our most definite imminent demise.

But the demise never came. There were some close calls, and a horrifying near miss involving a snowstorm and a cliff, but, for the most part, Bea and I were safe. We took down a railing or two, but no one died until Bea sputtered her last sputter and died herself, on the street, tenths of a mile from 200,000. A snowplow pushed her home. Her final glorious procession.

I donated Bea to a charity that helps rescue animals. They towed her away, but not before I ripped the Cherokee emblem off her back. It now sits on my nightstand where I can see it often and remember Bea fondly. Bea, you lovable, piece-of-shit, rusty, duct-taped death trap. I wonder if you are patio furniture now, or maybe the frame for a trendy new building, or maybe railroad tracks.

After my freshman year of college, still mourning the loss of Bea, it was time for me to buy a new car. I needed it to get to my summer job, interning at an insurance agency in the, you guessed it, auto claims department. With the help of my parents and some savings bonds that my great-grandma had left me, I bought a 2005 Volkswagen Golf, which I named Donna. I bottomed it out leaving the dealership, the first of the near nine gagillion times I would bottom that car out.

I had this nice new car that was zippy and handled like a dream, and I hardly drove it. I would drive to and from the insurance agency every day with the fear of a thousand devils in me that only increased with every horrific auto claim I worked on. Other than this twenty-minute commute, Donna sat in my driveway. More and more, it got harder for me to be in a car. Even when friends drove, I would have to lie down in the back seat in order to not have a panic attack.

Driving Donna from New Jersey to Amherst, Massachusetts, for the fall semester was a three-and-a-half-hour panic attack punctuated by tractor trailers whizzing by me at eighty miles per hour on Route 84. It took me a couple of hours after driving to stop shaking. So, until Thanksgiving, Donna sat in the parking lot at UMass, untouched, collecting leaves.

My friend Robbie loved to drive. He had a 2004 Audi A4 (Nigel) that was gorgeous and completely loaded. He drove me everywhere, and I trusted him. We drove around aimlessly quite a bit; we would drive fifteen miles out of town just to get the coffee we liked. I once vomited out of the side of Nigel on the highway on our way back from a party. If you are going to vomit out the side of a vehicle, might I recommend the Audi A4, because if you are going to puke, why not do it in luxury? I also vomited in my mom's 2006 A4 (Eli). She didn't pull over, so I puked in an envelope, which was slightly less luxurious.

Until I was twenty years old, I had crippling driving anxiety. This came to a head when I was driving home from spring break my junior year directly into a good, old fashioned, New England in early March, snow fuck, ice fuck, wind fuck, Nor' Easter. The snow started to really pick up when I hit Hartford. Cars were skidding off the road to the left and right of me. I must have seen thirty accidents that day. Cars in guardrails, cars in snow banks, and cars in other cars. I was too petrified to put my foot on the brake or the gas, so I rolled the 180 miles back to New Jersey. But I made it. I even made it down that steep hill with the railroad tracks in Little Falls. I had done it. I had operated a car in some of the worst driving conditions possible and survived, and so did the car. Fuck Yeah. I had made it home, mostly. There was no way I was getting my car up my steep and unplowed cul-de-sac. My sister had to back it up the hill. But I made it to my street, which is as good as home when you've got something to overcome.

From that moment, my driving anxiety vanished. I was steady behind the wheel. Now I just had to work on the other problem: I was, for lack of a better description, a shitty driver. I was that guy driving fifty in the fast lane and taking a hundred tries to pull into a parking spot. I extend my sincere apologies to everyone who ever had to drive behind me or be in a parking lot with me. But I was learning and getting better with ever mile I drove. Come my senior year of college, I was a great driver, carting my friends around Massachusetts winters with skill.

One Saturday, my senior year of college, I got a phone call from my best friend Robbie. He told me that our old roommate and close friend, Jane, had been killed in a car accident. She was driving up to Amherst for the weekend in a bad rainstorm; she had hydroplaned and hit a guardrail, and she was killed instantly at twenty-three years old. It was a punch right through my heart. The days following that phone call feel like a camera lens that keeps going in and out of focus, or like windshield wipers working double time in a rainstorm. Blurry: crying in my bedroom. Focus: taking flowers to the lake where Jane and I used to walk her dog. Blurry: driving to school Monday morning. Focus: running out of my acting class to cry on the bathroom floor of the theater department. Blurry: making plans with Robbie to drive out to Gloucester for her funeral. Focus: driving by the mangled guardrail on the Mass Pike. Blurry: what the hotel we stayed at was like. Focus: the overpowering smell of frankincense in the crowded seaside church. Blurry: the entire month after her funeral.

I was a wreck, barely functioning, on autopilot, drinking too much, sleeping too little, and surrounded by the thick fog of grief.

Then, one day I was on the bus on my way back to my apartment. It was late fall, and the bare trees were negative space against the sun setting over the Seven Sisters mountains. Tom Petty's "American Girl" played over my headphones, and I felt better. Better, a feeling that startled me as it cut through the miasma of grief. Better. OK. Breathing. Me again, well not quite me again but a different me, a me that had gone through something and come out on the other side. Better.

Later that year, I would sit in the passenger seat of a car, a boy's car. As my ass eased into the leather seats of his late '90s Saab, I had one of those unforgettable life moments, when the world stops for a small second and the universe agrees with you because you are exactly where you should be. I would spend hours as his passenger. The two of us were Earth-bound cosmonauts, flying down the backwoods valley highways at fast speeds, throwing beer bottles out the side, flicking cigarettes, and being young and ingeniously stupid.

Those were times. Times that felt like you could keep them forever. But you can't. These things shall end, and you shall go back to New Jersey, because you are a graduate and it's time to make good on that promise that you would do something with your life, and time to leave that boy behind in your tire tracks. "You got toll money?" he said. "EZ Pass." I said. But it wasn't easy for either of us. I got into the driver seat and made quick work of the 180 miles that stood between me and whatever would happen next.

I got a job, or what we, the recent post-grads of the great recession, call a job: an internship. I was interning with an off-off-Broadway theater company in New York City! Fuck yes, I had arrived. The hours were late, and the trains would stop running by the time I was done with work. Mass transit did not include me as part of the mass. So I had to be a driver, a New York City motherfucking driver. It was trial by fire; I had to get from point A to point B, and fast. The challenge is that between point A and point B exists the enemy, New York City. Traversing the grid of New York City takes nerves of steel. Cabbies on suicide missions, dumb tourists with the inability to understand that a large flashing orange hand means STOP WALKING INTO TRAFFIC, bikers begging you to take their lives, rip-your-hair-out traffic, and potholes that rattle your brain. You gotta be quick on the horn and quick on the brake. Never signal; it shows weakness. It's OK to hit cars. Don't leave a note, fuck notes and fuck you. And then there's parking. There is nowhere to park. It's better to just shove your car into your purse and carry it with you wherever you go because there is no way you are leaving it on the street without much well-calculated toil. I know how to park in New York City, I rarely get tickets, and I know how to fight 'em. I am not going to tell you how to park in New York City, because it's everyone for themselves, and I can't have you getting in my way and using my knowledge against me.

The internship turned into an actual job, and by actual job I mean that I get paid a small stipend to work full-time doing what I love. It's enough to pay for the tunnel tolls. I'm still working away in the insurance claims department to pay for the gas.

As I am writing this I am about to go pick up Donna, my not so trusty VW, from the shop. She's got almost 70,000 miles on her now. It's new brake pads and rotors this time. Some people leave their heart in San Francisco; I left my brakes in lower Manhattan.

I spend most of my life in my car now, waiting at the entrance to the Holland Tunnel. You can find me there, a twenty-five-year-old woman with her life on its way to being together, smearing on make up, talking on the phone to her lovely boyfriend, eating beef jerky, and frantically learning lines to plays. But if you look deep into my rearview mirror, with your eyes squinted just right, you'll see snowstorms and fearful not-yet adults; you'll see mangled guardrails with angel wings, and boys left behind in the dust, and maybe, if the mirror catches the sun just right, you'll see a 1984 Volvo flying through the air, bright-eyed kids inside, tempting a fate that hasn't caught up to them yet.

REACHING

████████████

(one night out)

BY ROB NEILL

We gathered. It was later in the day. Dusk, I would say. I was there with friends: that woman I used to hang out with, the one with the kabbalah tattoo; my roommate, Sasha; this other guy. There were several others. The Russian twins from Kursk, who I believe showed up late. We had had some mescal drinks at the bar. I really like the one with pickled hibiscus and the punches. No one was particularly hungry. The bar and the theater, you could call it a theater, were in adjacent brownstones on an often overlooked block—you would not know to go there for anything, if you did not know what was there, if someone had not told you. I could tell you more about how to find this place, if you want. Isn't that just always how it is?

Many of us that gathered that night did not know each other. We sat spread about the space in hard bentwood chairs. The ushers were particular, had crisp shirts, and did not let us move chairs much. There were lots of Christmas lights—which provided most of the lighting for the whole night. If I remember correctly we were lively, in a good mood, mostly, most probably due to the mescal.

There was a dog act, where the dogs actually played the kazoo. And a surprisingly tall contortionist. Near the middle of the show a sign lowered in from above; it read,

1. Walk Talking

A man—he had muttonchops and dressed like someone from the prohibition era who had lost his coat—walked into the space.

"One, walk-talking. And the English Beat is in the headset. It is sunny, breezy. And you like that. It's a start. So what if the post office, the bank, the noodle-house has closed already? You are not going to let that deter you. Other things are open. You are happy—happier each day. You get an iced coffee. It is raining somewhere, but you are jumping into the fray. Like the bluebird is on your shoulder and acting your consigliore. Here we go..."

He paused slightly putting two fingers on his right shoulder. One of the Russian twins, Vasily, took a pull off of a flask of something he did not share. I remember trying to picture a bluebird that was not a cartoon, but I failed.

A second sign,

2. Stickiness

lowered, the speaker moved closer to a clump of three in the audience and continued:

"Two, stickiness. People: always part of the equation." The speaker turned, pointing to an audience member across the room. "Hey, you like a good spaghetti dish? Do ya? With the sauce saucing things up?"

"Yes," said the woman.

"Sure," he jumped in. "I do too, and a little more red wine than the next sonabitch.

"And I think I know more now than I did yesterday—when I was jackin' it. And I can tell you things, things about 'do this,' 'make yourself a better so and so,' you might hear that from me. But what I tell you won't register unless the delivery system is something you can relate to. Yeah, I said, jackin' it. And if those things do not go against the core of who you think you are—the idea has personal stickiness for you, your peers—well, we would be movemoving to synergy or some shit."

The speaker clapped his hands and a third sign lowered.

3. Engagement

"Three, engagement." The speaker quickly sidled up to Sasha and knelt. "I'm gonna get on my knee for this one."

He looked deep into Sasha's gray eyes.

"You believe in the aliens?"

"I, I guess so."

"Sure, why the fuck not? You think they'd be good or bad relative to who we are—want things from us, want our trees, our babies, our souls... our JOBS?!?"

The speaker swept a finger pointing at much of the audience, and before Sasha really could respond, a fourth sign flipped below the third sign.

3.5. More Engagement

The speaker jumped up.

"Three point five, more engagement.

"For some reason I like the concept of an old fashioned panty raid; I think I understand where the folks of the '50s got off; why the '80s destroyed culture; and that we are spiralingdown compacting under all of this NOW that is barraging us unfiltered—TV on the Internet, movies on your phone, more books than you can read in a lifetime on your—who here fucking reads books anyway?"

Several of us responded—a few people raised a hand.

"Really? Many out there like games—they like to be engaged, always. While some of you here are thinking, 'He better not fucking touch ME!' But I am talking to all ya'll. Do you identify as a 'Millennial'? You?"

There were some nods. But the speaker was on a roll.

"I was raised to believe:"

He raised one finger, "You get into it, you better learn something."

He raised a second, "Don't fuck with it until you mastered it."

He raised a third, "Leave it better than you found it."

A fifth sign lowered quickly in—

4. New Ventures.

The speaker was now in the midst of us. He raised a fourth finger. "Four, new ventures. Not everyone needs the same information."

He grabbed a guy near us by the shoulder, got close to his face. "You want me to tell you something?"

He did not wait for an answer that was not coming. "I have missed a lot. A whole lifetime of lots."

He was now talking to all of us around him. "But there is so so much, my babies. I figure it this way: we need more secrets and not to know every bit of minutia—insta-fuckin-taneously. We need to circle-up more and download less. This old Italian filmmaker told me he's launching a movement against loneliness. Maybe that's a start. Hellllooo, Massimo, you magical madman, you go!

"We can do our part too. So I'll wrap up whispering just to you." And he was at my left ear and close, speaking softly: "I could see you tomorrow on the F-book; we could share some slo-mo cat videos. Or maybe you are just thinking, 'Why the fuck is he spitting in my ear?'"

I could feel the heat from his breath. I half nodded. The speaker stood up, "Could be both. Should be more." And he laughed, walking toward a curtain in the back. "Sure. That is better. And that's what we're at, here. I... we, may have gotten somewhere tonight..."

I thought he would say more, but he stopped and walked out.

We heard distinct, bell-like sounds from what turned out to be a glockenspiel. A curtain raised around the edge of the space revealing a band, of which the woman, Alex (Alex was her name), and the twins were big fans. This band, UnderFesler, is originally why we had come out that night. They oozed into the space, playing around us, playing upbeat accordion rock songs that often reveled in fish imagery and bouts of drinking slivovitz.

Things are hazier after that as we kept drinking mescal drinks. I recall a monkey who did card tricks, and us all singing along with an UnderFesler cover of "Barracuda."

Fortunately one, no, both of the twins lived nearby, so it was a short stumble to sleep. And the sleep was deep, and I recall that we woke up and had a greasy, eggy breakfast before moving too far into the next day. We eventually went back to our homes, our apartments. I cleaned out the oven, as it needed it, and then watched a *Law & Order* marathon. The next week started, and we went back to jobs that some of us only did to pay the bills.

The speaker's specific words did not initially stick with me, but then, about two weeks later, he sent me a message on Facebook. He sent me links, as promised, a variety actually, some to slo-mo cats, plus a link to UnderFesler's video for "I am Nemo: Captain of the Nautilus," in addition to a link that was a remastering of his speech with subtle underscoring.

I find that I like to listen to his recording sometimes, late at night. It is easy to get lost in his words and the patterns on the ceiling of my apartment from the lights of cars driving down the avenue. His voice has become familiar and assuring to me.

We did go back to the brownstones a couple more times—Sasha and I have a taste for mescal. We did not really get into the other performers and bands, and later that year the twins moved to Seattle. Now that I have watched many more cat videos, I wanted to let you know that I like the one where they are dressed up like ninjas the best, though I am still not sure if I am responsible enough yet to get my own cat. Maybe I will initiate a modicum of responsibility and start by getting a spider plant. I have begun studying Cantonese and am relearning to play the viola.

WHAT DOES IT MEAN TO BE A GROWN-UP?

"It's a certain marveling that you can do whatever you want, whenever you want.

It means eating ice cream sandwiches for breakfast in the heat of summer.

It means having expendable income to send younger siblings care packages.

It means waking up in the morning, putting your feet down, and wincing that your knees just aren't what they used to be.

It means finding out way too much about your parents' sex life."

—*Alison, 29, Saint-Exupéry Grown-Up*

DATA!

Average age virginity lost, as of 2002:

17

AN INTERVIEW

WITH A COUPLE WHO HAVE
TWO ADULT CHILDREN*
LIVING AT HOME

*(AGES TWENTY-FIVE AND TWENTY-SEVEN
AT TIME OF INTERVIEW)

Describe, in your own words, your family's living situation.

Father

My family, which includes my wife, myself, and two daughters, all reside together in our home in _____, New Jersey. We also own and share a vacation home in _____, New Jersey.

Mother

We are four adults, living most of the time in one home, but since we have a second home, sometimes we live there, too.

Is this (the two of them living with you as adults) something you thought would happen? If so, what are the differences from how you imagined it would be?

Father

I never had expectations in this regard. I am very much more of a "one step at a time" person, and, frankly, this arrangement has simply been the next step. I am happy that my wife and I have been able to provide a stable and safe place for each of our daughters to live while finding their place in this crazy world.

Mother

I never really gave it much thought. For a time, they were both away, so we developed a certain rhythm to our lives which we enjoyed. When they came back, one in 2008 and the other in 2010, that rhythm was disrupted, but we adapted. I will miss them when they go, but I will adjust to that as well.

What are some of the good and bad things about having your adult children live with you?

Mother

They could be better roommates—cleaning and picking up after themselves; they have to be reminded to do so, which is not what I expect from adults. There is certainly an added expense—gas, electric, water, food, household supplies—but we can absorb this cost. We are of the mind that as long as they are saving money, and by that I mean actually building up their bank accounts, we will not ask them for room and board. There is also a lack of privacy for us, although they are often away for weekends, which is good for all of us.

Father

There are really not many bad things...obviously, with four adults rushing to get off to work in the morning, showers could be hotter...but a new water heater seems to have resolved that issue effectively. Clutter is an issue—especially with a persistent "shoe-leaver" in the mix. On balance, however, I cherish the time spent with my now adult children and recognize that this "relationship proximity" can't last forever. Meals are always an adventure; friends (including boyfriends) are interesting and engaging; and the entertainment factor cannot be underrated! I love having them around.

Mother

I truly enjoy their company; they are bright, usually happy, and delightfully sociable. They will often cook dinners that are much more complicated than I have the time, energy, or inclination to whip up. They pick up the slack of caring for our dogs. I enjoy the company of their friends. I love seeing how they have matured from the children we raised into the wonderful women they have become.

What are some of the differences and similarities to living with both your daughters now compared to when they were children or teenagers?

Mother

They are certainly more cooperative and open to our advice than when they were teenagers. I guess having lived independently in college and even after, they have an idea of what it takes to make your way through life. They are more open about their relationships with others than when they were younger. I still worry when they are out late or driving long distances. I doubt that will ever change. I still have to remind them about things that need to be done around the house, and they have gotten better about actually doing them rather than shirking those responsibilities. They don't fight with one another the way they did when they were younger, but in some ways they still compete for our attention.

Father

I still love them both as I did during their teen-aged years, but now they are rational, positive, and considerate adults. And, I am not driving them anywhere!

What do you think of adult children living with their parents becoming quite common in the last few years?

Mother

The cost of living on your own in this area, even with a roommate, usually outstrips what young adults, even college-educated ones, can earn. What is different now compared to when I was younger is that parents of my generation frequently have better relationships with our children than we did with our parents. I can't ever conceive of hanging out with my parents unless it was a family event. That is not the case, at least in my home.

Father

Economic necessity creates simple realities. The cost of available housing, a rising population, and diminished work and career opportunities have real consequences. Those adult children who have parents who can provide an affordable, safe, and comfortable living arrangement are fortunate.

Do you worry about your daughters' economic futures? If so, in what ways?

Father

Without a vibrant manufacturing sector in this area, service sector opportunities—the staple of college-educated people—will stagnate. In the middle of a "down economy," and a long slide in middle class income, it is impossible not to be concerned. However, both daughters are enterprising, educated, skilled, and street-smart. I am hopeful.

Mother

I worry about everyone's economic futures, including my own, but I know we have raised them to be careful with money and to understand the need to work smart, hard, and at their best. If they should lose their jobs, I know that they have a cushion to tide them over, and I know they have the skills to get another job.

How about their personal futures (i.e., anything that doesn't involve having enough money)?

Father

I anticipate tough times ahead with commodity shortages and climate related concerns. Strong family ties are a bonus when new challenges create lifestyle and societal changes.

Mother

I have no worries about their personal futures, just hopes that they get to realize their dreams and aspirations, that they remain happy, productive, engaged, and hopeful.

What was your own process of moving out of your parents' house like?

Father

With three younger siblings in a much smaller house, moving out was not an option...it was a psychological necessity. I had always had a job, knew that I could not count on my parents for support going forward, and had to make my own way. I was in law school, was twenty-three, and it was time to get started. They were helpful and supportive—if not financially so. It was a much less expensive world in which to live.

Mother

After college, I came home, found a job, and within one year moved out and lived with a roommate. One year later, I had my own apartment, was working full time, and going to law school at night. I was twenty-three years old. I moved out and never looked back.

Where do you see the current living situation going in the next few months and/or years?

Mother

I expect that in the next year or so, both will have moved out and moved on with their lives.

Father

Our home is our family home and will remain so. All are and will be welcome. I suspect, however, that both daughters have other ideas regarding their living arrangements going forward...

PAINKILLERS

BY BRIAN JAMES POLAK

A hospital room. Night.

NARRATOR

Once upon a time, there was a story about a brother and sister and a dream they shared. And, one night, here in this hospital room, the story ended. To say their dream came true would be misleading. When this dream ended, it transformed into something else. And it left one of them alone for the first time.

LITTLE BROTHER

Big Sister, I need you.

BIG SISTER

I'm still here, Little Brother. We'll do this together. Like always.

LITTLE BROTHER

That's not good enough. Not anymore. We've been pushing for so long. No more. Nobody floats on a cloud. I know that now. Everybody disappears. I don't want you to disappear.

BIG SISTER

I won't disappear. I'm going to float away on a cloud, Little Brother. It'll be the most beautiful thing you've ever seen. I'll float away on a cloud. This time will be different.

LITTLE BROTHER

You've said that before. I'm older now. I'm wise. After all this time, I've never seen—

BIG SISTER

This is a promise. I'll never break a promise. Push out onto the clouds all the pain. There's too much pain. There's nothing anybody can do. Only you can help me. I'm going to float away on a cloud. "Push out onto the clouds all the pain" is what Daddy said. Remember? Push out onto the clouds all the pain. It'll be beautiful. I'll be wearing the most amazing white dress, with flowers in my hands like the day Mommy and Daddy got married. And I'll be smiling. I'll be smiling as I float away. And I'll tell you how much I love you one last time before I disappear. I need you to help me. Move my bed closer to the window.

NARRATOR

He moves her closer to the window.

BIG SISTER

Here, Little Brother, put your hands on my hips.

LITTLE BROTHER

No pillow?

BIG SISTER

No pillow. Not this time. That's good there. We're gonna do this together. Like always.

LITTLE BROTHER

And this time...

BIG SISTER

I'll float away and you'll see.

LITTLE BROTHER

Promise.

BIG SISTER

Promise. Open the window. Take my arm. Help me up.

NARRATOR

As Big Sister stands in the window she remembers all the people she's touched over the years and for the first time she wonders...

BIG SISTER

I need a push. Just a little push is all I need.

LITTLE BROTHER

I want to know what it's like.

BIG SISTER

You will. Push. Push. Push.

NARRATOR

Little Brother gently pushes her out the window and into the air. We hear the sound of a heart monitor go to flat-line. He watches her float away on a cloud and remains still until she fades out of sight. He looks as if all of his most magical dreams finally came true. And, in a way, they have. But over time, his happiness gives way to loneliness. He stands on the edge of the window, takes a deep breath and— The flat-line continues. A time earlier. Big Sister and Little Brother stand above a hospital bed, each grasping a white pillow.

Hospital patient lies in the bed, covered by a white sheet. His face cannot be seen.

BIG SISTER

I'm not well, Little Brother. I need your strength. I can barely breath. Help me push harder.

LITTLE BROTHER

I'm pushing.

BIG SISTER

My lungs are burning. I can't do this alone.

LITTLE BROTHER

Burning how bad?

BIG SISTER

Burning like Daddy. Help me push. This man's still breathing. Be strong for me.

LITTLE BROTHER

I'm strong. For you.

NARRATOR

They push. We hear the sound of a heart monitor go to flat-line. Big Sister is not well. She falls onto the bed. Little Brother is concerned. He doesn't know what to do to help her. The flat-line continues. A time earlier. They stand above a hospital bed with pillows in their hands.

BIG SISTER

Grab the pillow. Push.

LITTLE BROTHER

She's kicking. Why is she kicking? I don't like when they kick.

BIG SISTER

She's fighting. She's so strong. She doesn't know where she'll be going. So much beauty. She'll know soon. Push the pillow harder. She'll stop kicking.

LITTLE BROTHER

The picture on her nightstand. That's her little baby. I don't...I don't want to do this anymore. They don't float, Big Sister. I know they don't. You said they'd float.

BIG SISTER

Shhh. Don't stop. She's so close. It'll be better. Just push. I don't have the strength...

Big Sister coughs.

LITTLE BROTHER

Your cough is getting worse. I don't want...*(to do this any longer)*

BIG SISTER

Shhhhh. Push out onto the clouds. Push.

NARRATOR

They push. We hear the sound of the flat-line. A time earlier.

They stand above a hospital bed with pillows in their hands.

LITTLE BROTHER

I've never seen them float, Big Sister.

NARRATOR

They push. Flat-line

A time earlier. They stand above a hospital bed with pillows in their hands.

LITTLE BROTHER
Just once.

NARRATOR
They push. Flat-line

A time earlier. They stand above a hospital bed with pillows in their hands.

LITTLE BROTHER
...on a cloud.

BIG SISTER
Shhhh.

NARRATOR
They push. Flat-line.

A time earlier. They stand above a hospital bed with pillows in their hands.

BIG SISTER
Push.

NARRATOR
They push. Flat-line.

A time earlier. They stand above a hospital bed with pillows in their hands.

LITTLE BROTHER
A little girl.

BIG SISTER
She's in pain, Little Brother.

LITTLE BROTHER
She's my age. She could be my friend. She's so beautiful just the way she is, Big Sister.

BIG SISTER
She'll look even more beautiful sailing away on a cloud. This one can be your angel.

LITTLE BROTHER
Promise?

BIG SISTER
Promise. Push.

NARRATOR
They push. Flat-line. The story continues a time earlier—

They stand above a hospital bed with pillows in their hands.

BIG SISTER
Are you ready?

LITTLE BROTHER
We don't even know him. My stomach aches.

BIG SISTER
He's got a little boy who loves him just like you loved Daddy. Place the pillow on his face.

LITTLE BROTHER
I hope we see...

BIG SISTER
Push.

NARRATOR

They push. Flat-line. Sweet and dark naivety. The miracle of sadness motivates the gentlest creatures to perform dastardly acts with a dream as fuel. The flat-line continues. A time earlier. They stand above a hospital bed with pillows in their hands.

LITTLE BROTHER

When do we stop?

BIG SISTER

When he quits breathing.

LITTLE BROTHER

He was barely breathing when we started.

NARRATOR

We hear the sound of a heart monitor go to flat-line.

BIG SISTER

I think that's good enough. Move the pillow.

LITTLE BROTHER

Is he breathing?

BIG SISTER

No.

LITTLE BROTHER

Are we done?

BIG SISTER

Not sure. I think so. Daddy?

LITTLE BROTHER

Dad? Daddy? Are you breathing? Do you really think he'll float away on a cloud like he said?

BIG SISTER

I do. There are more people like him in this hospital, Little Brother. We could help them too.

LITTLE BROTHER

Does everybody float away on clouds when they go?

BIG SISTER

I think so. I think they do. Daddy said so. Let's help them float. It will be so beautiful.

LITTLE BROTHER

I want to see. I never got to see Mommy. I want to see! Let's help others.

NARRATOR

The flat-line continues. A time earlier. They stand above a hospital bed with pillows in their hands for the very first time. We find ourselves at the beginning of the story. Once upon a time, a mother lies helpless on a bed—

Hospital Patient in the bed rises and takes a pillow into his hands. This is Father. Narrator gets into bed. She is Mother.

LITTLE BROTHER

I don't understand, Big Sister. What's Daddy doing? He put a pillow on her face.

BIG SISTER

Her lungs. They burn her.

LITTLE BROTHER
She can't breathe?

BIG SISTER
It hurts. Daddy said her medicine won't work. We can make it better.

LITTLE BROTHER
But she can't breathe.

BIG SISTER
There's too much pain. He says there's nothing anybody can do. That only we can help her. Daddy told me, Little Brother, that Mommy's going to float away on a cloud. Push out onto the clouds all the pain is what he said. He said it'll be beautiful. She'll be wearing the most amazing white dress, with flowers in her hands like the day they got married. And she'll be smiling. She'll be smiling as she floats away. And she'll tell us how much she loves us one last time before she disappears. Daddy needs us to help him. Here, Little Brother, put your hands on the pillow. Push.

LITTLE
Push?

BIG SISTER
Push. Push. Push.

They push. Heart monitor goes flat then fades away. Light fades to black.

END OF PLAY

AFTERMATH

BY SARAH C. JONES

Everyone clapped when Kyle raised the first slice of cake in the air. "Congratulations!" a few people yelled. Paul whooped and bumped into Tanya, who fell onto the couch laughing as one of her cardboard bat wings scraped James.

"I can't believe Kyle bought himself a cake," Claire whispered to Sheri.

"I can't believe he got them to write 'Happy Employment' on it," Sheri whispered back.

"He can get whatever dumb shit he wants as long as he buys us booze," said Paul. "It's not like we know anyone else with a job." He reached for the punch bowl, where scoops of pink sherbet hissed quietly in the cheap vodka. He filled two plastic champagne flutes and walked over to the couch. "How've you been, Tanya?" he asked as he handed one of the cups to Marie.

"What animal are you supposed to be?" asked Marie as, on the other side of the room, someone's cousin from Albuquerque turned off the lights and Michael turned on the stereo.

No one really wanted cake. A piece fell from the coffee table and was trampled and smeared as the center of the living room gradually became a dance floor. It was dark and hot, even after Estelle propped open the balcony door. Within a few minutes of the lights going off everyone was dancing with an overflowing cup in hand. Estelle and James, who had taken off their matching tiger tails, periodically broke away from the tightly packed crowd to stand over the stereo and argue about the next song, half-yelling and half-miming.

"I mean, what kind of an asshole throws a party for himself? Just because he finally found a real job. No one else has anything to celebrate." Claire looked around cautiously.

"Yeah," Sheri said. "Did you remember your antlers?"

"They're in my backpack."

"Do my ears look OK?"

"Don't worry, Sheri. You're the best-looking rat in the room. Maybe Kyle should have dressed up as a rat. A slimy corporate rat," said Claire, trying not to laugh before she finished her sentence.

As the living room got warmer and damper, the mosquitoes wandered in. Paul accidentally smashed one between his arm and Marissa's shoulder, but he barely noticed as he tried to casually position himself behind Claire. Kyle was trying to stay as far away from her as possible, but James pushed him in Claire's direction as he tried to grab Julie, whose silver rabbit ears were slipping from her damp hair. The bass thumped hard enough to send vibrations through the floor and up the dancers' legs, but it wasn't quite loud enough for the neighbors to have reason to call the police.

"But I just think this party is a bad idea!" Claire gesticulated wildly at Sheri. "It's inconsiderate."

"It's fine. All our friends are here, drunk and dressed as animals."

"I'm tired of Kyle's smug face with those stupid whiskers drawn on it."

"You broke up two years ago. Come on."

Claire put down her plastic cup. Her jaw looked stiff. She turned away suddenly. "I'm going to get some beer," she called over her shoulder.

By the time Diane, Eric, and Christine showed up, most of the dancers' face paint had dripped down their necks and onto their costumes. The new arrivals laughed as they were quickly pulled into the heaving crowd. The whites of Paul's eyes seemed to glow from the center of the black grease paint he had smeared over and under his lids in an effort to look like a raccoon. When Diane saw that Julie had pushed James up against the wall and was kissing his neck, she raised the punch bowl to her own mouth and drank with heaving gulps.

Marissa fell in the middle of the dance floor and almost took Eric down with her. Paul and Christine carried her to the bathroom, and between that and the drinking and the dancing no one noticed Kyle and Sheri sneak off to the kitchen, where they kissed a few times before looking at each other in horror but not surprise.

Tony and James were the first to sit down, so they got the couch. Eric and Diane went home together as usual, and Paul and Marissa left quietly. Sheri's eyes seemed slightly swollen as she and Claire left arm-in-arm. Someone turned the volume down until the music was inaudible, but the stereo was still on. Kyle had passed out in his bed, black face paint streaked across his face, before the last guests lifted their bags from the sticky floor and rubbed their eyes under the bright lights in the hallway.

WHAT DOES IT MEAN TO BE A GROWN-UP?

"You appreciate the value of a midday nap.

One of your favorite foods is a vegetable.

You hate cleaning the house because your parents don't give you money for doing it anymore, but you do it anyway because you're embarrassed about what your other grown-up friends will think when they come over.

You don't like getting too drunk, because you can't deal with the hangovers anymore. Nevertheless, you wish it were socially acceptable to always be two drinks in. Especially at work.

You no longer make Christmas or birthday lists. If you want something, you just buy it, and if you can't afford it, you convince yourself you didn't really want it anyway.

You refuse to pay full price for anything because A) you KNOW someone, somewhere sells it for less, and B) you equate spending responsibly with spending as little as possible at all times because C) you have bills and rent to pay.

You constantly tell outrageous lies to small children, and they believe you without question."

—*Ruth, 24, student and reluctant grown-up*

 Average age of Best Actress winner is 36. Best Actor is 44.

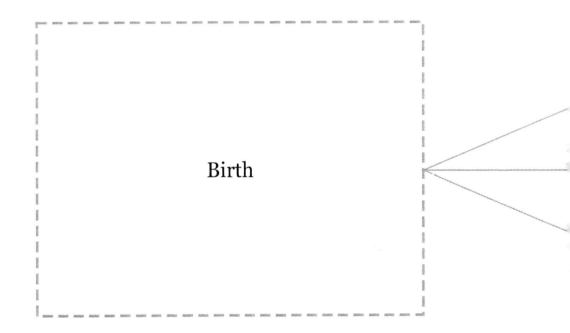

Birth

WHAT IT MEANS TO BE A GROWN-UP: A FLOWCHART

BY JOSEPH FINK

There is a time that is the first time you feel sad.

Darkness, as sheltering womb.

Paul Simon albums.

You wake your parents in the middle of the night to ask them to list foods eaten at Thanksgiving.

Rain.

Everyone who is older than you is old.

The first novel you ever read, which is about aliens pretending to be teachers.

How the world looks from the bottom of a swimming pool.

Nestling. Lots of nestling. In arms, mostly.

Aware of your own breath, you keep yourself alive until you can forget again.

From the train you see, through the broken windows of an abandoned warehouse, the silhouette of a man seated by himself at a table in the middle of an empty and dark room. A moment later he is gone. You will never learn anything more about who he is.

Perfect vision, no comprehension. The world, in sharp focus and fathomless.

That time you saw a little girl inside a minivan beating on the window, looking scared. You were little too, and did nothing.

Baby wipes.

Eggs, scrambled.

Everyone who is older than you is huge.

There is a time that is the first time you feel happy.

Smelling without reference to the source of the smell, so the odor itself is a discrete object. You will unlearn this.

You have no way of telling the difference between the imaginary and the real. The world is more interesting but also full of monsters.

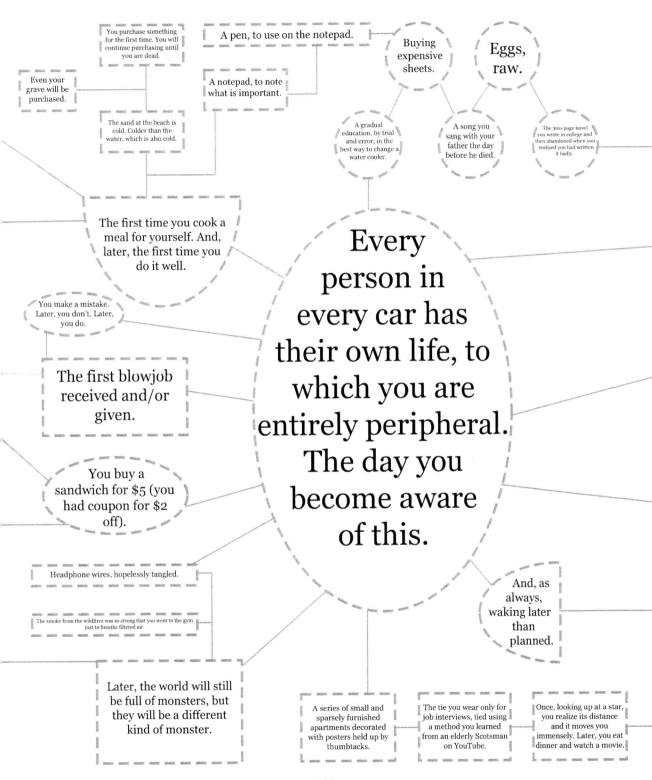

You purchase something for the first time. You will continue purchasing until you are dead.

A pen, to use on the notepad.

Buying expensive sheets.

Eggs, raw.

Even your grave will be purchased.

A notepad, to note what is important.

The sand at the beach is cold. Colder than the water, which is also cold.

A gradual education, by trial and error, in the best way to change a water cooler.

A song you sang with your father the day before he died.

The 300-page novel you wrote in college and then abandoned when you realized you had written it badly.

The first time you cook a meal for yourself. And, later, the first time you do it well.

You make a mistake. Later, you don't. Later, you do.

The first blowjob received and/or given.

Every person in every car has their own life, to which you are entirely peripheral. The day you become aware of this.

You buy a sandwich for $5 (you had coupon for $2 off).

Headphone wires, hopelessly tangled.

The smoke from the wildfires was so strong that you went to the gym just to breathe filtered air.

And, as always, waking later than planned.

Later, the world will still be full of monsters, but they will be a different kind of monster.

A series of small and sparsely furnished apartments decorated with posters held up by thumbtacks.

The tie you wear only for job interviews, tied using a method you learned from an elderly Scotsman on YouTube.

Once, looking up at a star, you realize its distance and it moves you immensely. Later, you eat dinner and watch a movie.

191

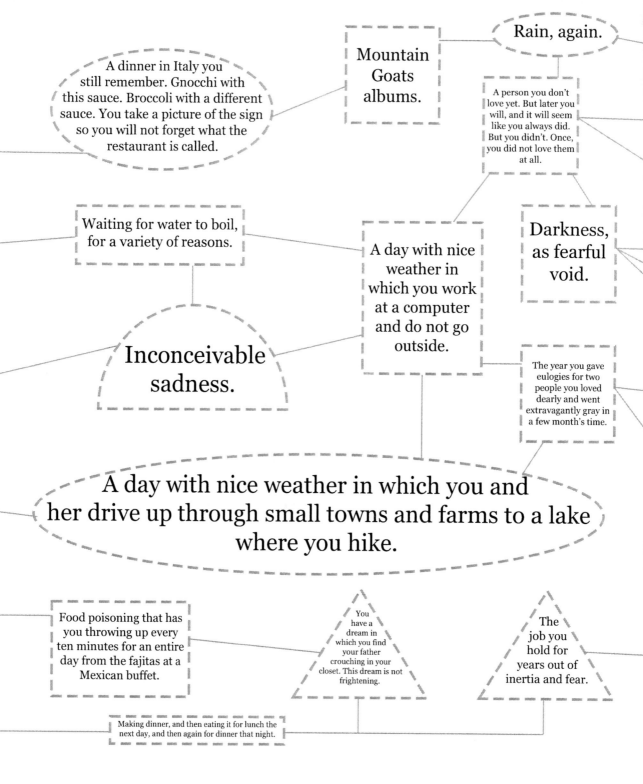

Rain, again.

Mountain Goats albums.

A dinner in Italy you still remember. Gnocchi with this sauce. Broccoli with a different sauce. You take a picture of the sign so you will not forget what the restaurant is called.

A person you don't love yet. But later you will, and it will seem like you always did. But you didn't. Once, you did not love them at all.

Waiting for water to boil, for a variety of reasons.

A day with nice weather in which you work at a computer and do not go outside.

Darkness, as fearful void.

Inconceivable sadness.

The year you gave eulogies for two people you loved dearly and went extravagantly gray in a few month's time.

A day with nice weather in which you and her drive up through small towns and farms to a lake where you hike.

Food poisoning that has you throwing up every ten minutes for an entire day from the fajitas at a Mexican buffet.

You have a dream in which you find your father crouching in your closet. This dream is not frightening.

The job you hold for years out of inertia and fear.

Making dinner, and then eating it for lunch the next day, and then again for dinner that night.

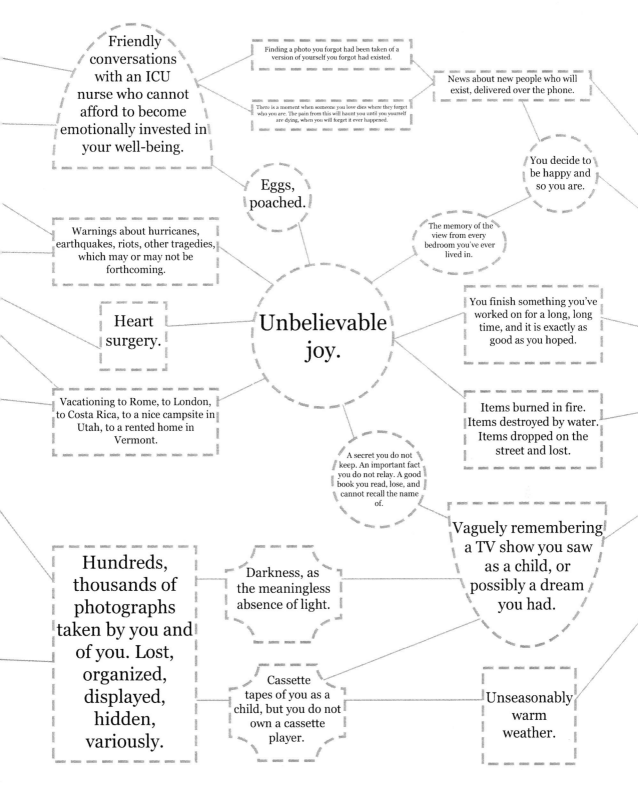

Friendly conversations with an ICU nurse who cannot afford to become emotionally invested in your well-being.

Finding a photo you forgot had been taken of a version of yourself you forgot had existed.

News about new people who will exist, delivered over the phone.

There is a moment when someone you love dies where they forget who you are. The pain from this will haunt you until you yourself are dying, when you will forget it ever happened.

You decide to be happy and so you are.

Eggs, poached.

Warnings about hurricanes, earthquakes, riots, other tragedies, which may or may not be forthcoming.

The memory of the view from every bedroom you've ever lived in.

Unbelievable joy.

You finish something you've worked on for a long, long time, and it is exactly as good as you hoped.

Heart surgery.

Vacationing to Rome, to London, to Costa Rica, to a nice campsite in Utah, to a rented home in Vermont.

Items burned in fire. Items destroyed by water. Items dropped on the street and lost.

A secret you do not keep. An important fact you do not relay. A good book you read, lose, and cannot recall the name of.

Vaguely remembering a TV show you saw as a child, or possibly a dream you had.

Hundreds, thousands of photographs taken by you and of you. Lost, organized, displayed, hidden, variously.

Darkness, as the meaningless absence of light.

Cassette tapes of you as a child, but you do not own a cassette player.

Unseasonably warm weather.

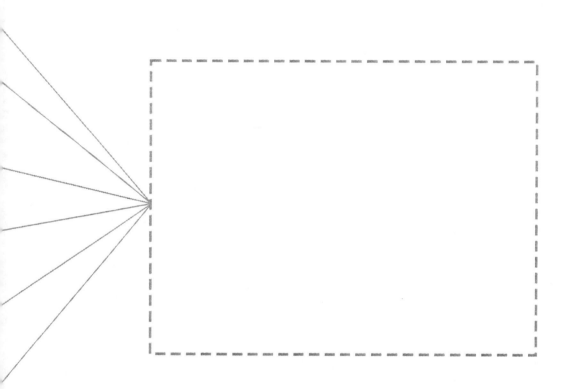

ACKNOWLEDGEMENTS

First off, a huge thank you to my girlfriend, who was extremely helpful and understanding in the long and turbulent process of putting this book together.

Thank you also to her family and to my family. Both make life significantly more worth living.

Other thanks:

All of the writers who contributed work to this project, as well as all the people who took the time to give short thoughts about being a grown-up.

Hannah Lott-Schwartz, whose experience with editing was invaluable. For more information about her freelance editing work, go to itsaseahorse.com.

Justin Marquis, who designed a fantastic cover on fantastically short notice. To learn more about his art and other cool things, go to scrollingmarquis.com.

Daniel McCoy, who researched all the **DATA!** factoids throughout the book.

Twitter, Facebook, and every other way of connecting to random people on the Internet, seeing potential in them, and asking if they'd like to try writing something for a book.

The New York Neo-Futurists, a collective which had a profound effect on my outlook on both life and art, and from which several of the contributors of this book originate. You should check out their weekly show in New York City. Their website is nynf.org.

SomethingAwful.com, which gave me my first real writing job, and which still, twelve years in, churns out a remarkable amount of worthwhile material on an insanely regular schedule.

Bad Wolf Press, the company my father co-founded, dedicated to publishing educational musicals for children to perform. Although he is no longer with us, the company has continued, and if you work with children, or know someone who does, you should check out badwolfpress.com.

And finally, you. Books are nothing without a reader. I mean, I hope you got something out of it too, but thanks.

WHAT IS COMMONPLACE BOOKS?

Commonplace Books is, among other things, you.

We are here to help express the global arts community that has formed over the last few years on the Internet. We are about finding interesting and talented people, wherever they are in the world and in their careers, and helping them find a larger audience through communal projects and playful challenges.

Our first book, *A Commonplace Book of the Weird: The Untold Stories of H. P. Lovecraft*, found an audience all over the world and continues to be discovered by new readers to this day. We are proud and grateful for the unbelievable reception that book found.

Here is a simple fact: it is a better time to be an artist now than any other time in history. Whether you are a writer or a painter or a musician or a filmmaker, you were born at a lucky time. Thanks to the Internet, global distribution and organization is now available to everyone.

The exact model for how all this should work isn't settled yet. But that is why it is up to us, the artists of this generation, the generation living in the best time in history to be an artist, to create the world that we want to live in. To create the models to function in that world.

This is the world of Kickstarter and WikiLeaks. It is a world full of risk, but with the possibility for rewards unlike any that have existed before. And Commonplace Books was made for exactly that world.

Even in the midst of an endless economic crisis, even as things get harder every year, it is always possible to find great artists and help them reach an audience.

Every person reading this is part of Commonplace Books, and I can't wait to see what we do next.

*Please go to **commonplacebooks.com** to get in touch, to join our mailing list, or to check out what else all of us are doing.*

AUTHOR BIOS

Kathleen Akerley is a DC-based playwright whose produced works include *Theories of the Sun, Something Past in Front of the Light, The Oogatz Man, 1,952 Miles* and a stage adaptation of Kurt Vonnegut's *Cat's Cradle*. She has also worked as a sports writer covering the National Hockey League. Kathleen is a member of the playwriting collective Lizard Claw.

Meg Bashwiner is a writer, performer and co-artistic director of the New York Neo-Futurists. The New York Neo-Futurists are an ensemble of wildly creative theater makers best known for their hit show *Too Much Light Makes the Baby Go Blind* running every weekend in NYC. More info at www.nynf.org. Meg is a writer, performer, designer and producer whose work has been seen at The Monkey, The Kraine Theater, HERE Arts Center, Theater for the New City, The Ontological-Hysteric Theater and Chicago's Neo Futurarium. She holds a B.A in Theater from UMass Amherst. She has a very grown up crush on Joseph Fink.

Etan Berkowitz is an East coast gentleman settling into his West coast dream, enjoying his California king-size bed immensely. Most of his time is occupied with finding the best new cheap-eats in the city, propagating his experience on various social media channels and raking in that e-money. An early adopter of all kinds, he'll try anything once. A New York City native and NYU graduate, Etan is trying to bring his tech-startup dreams to fruition.

Kevin Bowen is a judgmental washed-up minor Internet celebrity/troll with a strange nose who watched too many episodes of *Mad Men* and possibly as a result now works in the NYC advertising industry.

Marcy Braidman was born in Northern California, on May Day, and in the eighties. This all means that she was destined to love sunshine and bright colors. She also loves mermaids and pirates and enjoys filling peoples' heads with nonsense and creating mischief. She has trouble taking anything seriously for an extended period of time and promises to never ever really grow up. To spend some time reading more of her writing, go to streaksofiction.blogspot.com.

J Chastain lives and works in theme parks across America. He has drawn comics for a site called Monsterkillers and he also has a Twitter.

Jeffrey Cranor writes, performs, and directs (mostly short) plays for the New York Neo-Futurists and their long-running show *Too Much Light Makes the Baby Go Blind*. He co-wrote & performed in 2008's full-length Neo-Futurist show *(Not) Just a Day Like Any Other*, for which he won a NY Innovative Theater award for Outstanding Ensemble. That same year, his 10-minute play *I'm Not Here* (featuring the NY Neos) was chosen for performance in *Occurence* at Ars Nova, alongside original work by Tommy Smith, Reggie Watts, and Mike Daisey. In 2009, Jeffrey co-wrote and directed Jillian Sweeney's solo show *This Could Be It* at The Chocolate Factory. And in 2011, Jeffrey performed in and co-wrote *What the Time Traveler Will Tell Us* with Joseph Fink. This is Jeffrey's second short story contribution to Commonplace Books.

Joseph Fink is a writer and editor who lives, surprisingly, in Brooklyn. He oversees just about everything at Commonplace Books, and is looking forward to moving it forward with ever more ambitious and exciting projects. He also does theater occasionally, having recently performed in and co-wrote *What the Time Traveler Will Tell Us* with Jeffrey Cranor.

Found Magazine collects found stuff: love letters, birthday cards, kids' homework, to-do lists, ticket stubs, poetry on napkins, doodles —anything that gives a glimpse into someone else's life. Visit them at foundmagazine.com.

Cara Francis is a writer, director, performer, and ensemble-member of the New York Neo-Futurists, writing for, designing and performing in *Too Much Light Makes the Baby Go Blind*, *The Soup Show*, *(un)afraid* and *The Complete and Condensed Stage Directions of Eugene O'Neill, Volume One: Early Plays/Lost Plays*. (The Kraine Theater, Barrow Street Theatre, Arena Stage). Cara has performed and had her work produced at The Old Vic, The Public, HERE, The Flea, The Brick, Dixon Place, The Bushwick Starr, Galapagos Art Space, and The Bowery Poetry Club and was a Spring 2009 Short Form Artist in Residency at the Ontological-Hysteric.

Kevin R. Free is a writer-performer who's told stories on NPR, Dana Rossi's the Soundtrack Series, and on the mainstage at The Moth. An alumnus of the New York Neo-Futurists, he wrote over 60 plays for *Too Much Light Makes the Baby Go Blind*, and his full-length Neo-Futurist play, *(Not) Just a Day Like Any Other*, co-written with Christopher Borg, Jeffrey Cranor, and Eevin Hartsough, was the recipient of the NY IT Award for Outstanding Ensemble in 2009. One of NYTheatre.com's People of the year in 2010, his full-length plays, *Face Value* and *A Raisin in the Salad: Black Plays for White People*, were published by indietheaternow.com. To read more of his thoughts, visit him @kevinrfree on Twitter, or at kevinrfree.com.

Genevra Gallo-Bayiates is still figuring out what she wants to be when she grows up. She currently works as Assistant Director in the Career Advancement Center at Lake Forest College, while simultaneously serving as the Communication Specialist & Message Strategist for the Plays for Presidents Festival 2012. She is an accomplished choreographer, writer, performer, and educator, a Neo-Futurist alum, and published author (Playscripts, Inc; Hope and Nonthings Publishing; Beyond Words Publishing). She lives in the Chicago area with her husband and colleague, Andy Bayiates, their beautiful daughter and greatest creation, Ariana, and a crazy-yet-cute Boston Terrier named Simon.

Marcus Goodyear is Senior Editor for TheHighCalling.org and author of the award-winning poetry collection *Barbies at Communion*. He lives in the Texas hill country with his wife, two children, two dogs, a frog, a few fish, and a herd of deer that eat everything they plant in their yard.

Neil Hamburger is America's Funnyman, bringing live comedy anywhere a laugh is needed.

Eevin Hartsough is an actor and writer living in NYC. Since 2006 she has been an ensemble member with the New York Neo-Futurists with/for whom she has co-written three full-length theater pieces - *You Are In an Open Field* (2012); *Laika Dog in Space* (2010); *(Not) Just a Day Like Any Other* (2009) and authored countless short pieces for their signature show *Too Much Light Makes the Baby Go Blind*. Eevin is currently at work on a new full-length play in the Absurdist tradition, titled *The Mother of Us All*. More info at EevinHartsough.com.

Sarah C. Jones is a reader, writer, grad student, and librarian living in Brooklyn, NY.

Kyle Kinane has been up and at it for almost half his life, mostly searching for what "it" might be. He was called "bleak and misanthropic" by the London Evening Standard, which he still feels may be a compliment. He is a comedian.

Jacquelyn Landgraf is an actress, director, and writer based in Brooklyn, New York. Since 2005, she has been a member of the New York Neo-Futurists. She has a B.F.A. in Drama from NYU's Tisch School of the Arts.

Veronica Liu is a writer and illustrator, as well as cofounder of Fractious Press, the online station Washington Heights Free Radio, and Word Up community bookshop. She works as an editor at Seven Stories Press.

Daniel McCoy is a New York-based writer and performer whose plays, including *Eli and Cheryl Jump*, *Group*, and *The Downtown Daylight Project*, have been produced in

NYC and around the country. Other plays, including *Sympathy, Sheila St. George and the World's Farthest Falling Man*, and *Goddamn Gorgeous Mess*, have received readings and workshops as well. As a member of the New York Neo-Futurists, he has produced over 70 short plays for the late-night show *Too Much Light Makes the Baby Go Blind* and received a New York Innovative Theatre award nomination for Outstanding Performance Art Production for *(un)afraid*, which he co-wrote and performed in at The Living Theatre in 2010. His short story, "DISSIPATION?", was published in *A Commonplace Book of the Weird: The Untold Stories of H. P. Lovecraft*. Daniel is from Portland, Oregon, and spent a healthy number of years in Los Angeles, where he is a member-at-large of the award-winner Elephant Theatre Company. He recently received his BA in English from Brooklyn College.

Rob Neill is a founding member and the Managing Director of the New York Neo-Futurists, and he has performed *Too Much Light Makes the Baby Go Blind* around the country since 1995. Rob has worked at the Ontological in the Incubator and Tiny Theater, created original pieces for PS 122's *Avant-Garde-Arama* and Vampire Cowboys' *Revamped* produced *The 6-Pack* and *Apocalypse Neo* at the Kraine, and co-created *Laika Dog in Space*. Rob continues to write and perform in *Too Much Light...*, works some days in the commercial industry, and has several of his plays and poems published. He trained at the London Academy of Music and Dramatic Art, the National Theater Institute, and Grinnell College.

Zack Parsons is a Chicago area writer known for his acerbic commentary and bleakly humorous science fiction. He has authored two non-fiction books, *My Tank Is Fight!* and *Your Next-Door Neighbor Is a Dragon*. His debut novel, *Liminal States*, was released in April of 2012.

Brian James Polak is a playwright living in Los Angeles, CA.

Sam Pow has been working in social services for the last seven years. He currently helps manage a transitional housing program for homeless, post-incarcerated recovering addicts who have mental health diagnoses and are living with HIV. He provides his 48 clients with counseling, conflict resolution, and crisis intervention. Earlier in his career, Sam worked with teenage foster girls living in group homes. Sam plays drums in the LA-based bands The Warlords of Rock and Roll Thunder and Lightning and Solar Flare. *No Choice* is his first short story. He is working on writing song lyrics and learning to play the vibes. Sam hopes to one day launch a one-man band called Flower Pow and the Good Vibes as a singer-songwriter-vibist. He lives in a small canyon on the outskirts of Los Angeles with his dear wife, Anna.

Nathan Rabin was the first, and is, to date, the only head writer for A.V Club, the entertainment section of satirical newspaper The Onion, where he has been employed for the last fifteen years. He is the author of *The Big Rewind: A Memoir Brought to You by Pop Culture* (Scribner), *My Year of Flops: One Man's Journey Deep into the Heart of Cinematic Failure* (Scribner), an upcoming coffee-table book about "Weird Al" Yankovic for Abrams Image, and a book about musical subcultures focusing on Phish and Insane Clown Posse also for Scribner. He is still working through some shit.

Marta Rainer has performed her solo show *Unaccustomed to My Name* Off-Broadway, across America and internationally since 2001. A founding ensemble member of the New York Neo-Futurists (NY Innovative Theatre Award, Outstanding Performance Art), Marta is also an award-winning stage actress who is nevertheless proud of her cameo as "Woman with Groceries" in College Humor's *We Are the 1%* video. Collaborators include composer Elena Ruehr, and directors Paul Sills and Slava Dolgachev. She is a published writer of fiction (*A Commonplace Book of the Weird: The Untold Stories of H.P. Lovecraft*) and her non-fiction writing includes profiles of stonemasons in *The Stone Primer* (Storey Publishing), and numerous magazine features, including a cover story (Small Room Decorating) on the skinniest house in America. Marta's first feature screenplay *Radio Cape Cod* (2009) debuted on PBS on Valentine's Day. Currently on faculty at New York Film Academy, Marta has taught acting/playwriting at several institutions, including both her almae matres: New Actors Workshop/Antioch University McGregor and Wellesley College. She lives in Brooklyn with her husband Paul.

Joey Rizzolo is a performer and award-winning playwright with the New York Neo-Futurists where he has, to date, premiered hundreds of short plays (*The Giving Car* among them), and one long play. He has also premiered full-length work at some very fancy theaters (the Kennedy Center among them), and his plays can be found in print in various compilations (this one among them).

Greg Rutter is an Emmy Award winning writer who works at the advertising agency Wieden + Kennedy in Portland, Oregon. He is a regular contributor to *The Onion* and the IFC show *The Onion News Network*. In 2009 he was the keynote speaker at ROFLCon, speaking about mainstreaming the web after his website YouShouldHaveSeenThis.com went viral. Sorry ladies, but he lives with his wife in Portland and they have lots of friends and go to lots of parties. Also, you can tell he works out. He owns a cat who is not very nice at all.

Mobutu Sese Seko founded the blog MrDestructo.com. He is a political blogger for Gawker and a contributor to GQ.com, Vice.com, and SomethingAwful.com. He recently remodeled his entire kitchen.

Lusia Strus is a writer and actor whose work has been seen on small and big stages, and small and big screens.

Leah Nanako Winkler is a playwright, essayist and director from Kamakura, Japan, and Lexington, KY. Her plays have been produced and/or seen at venues such as The Brick Theater, The Incubator Arts Project/Ontological Hysteric Theater, 3LD Technology Center, Magic Futurebox, Ars Nova, The Ensemble Studio Theater, Dixon Place, HERE arts Center, New Georges, New York Theater Workshop, Asian American Writers Workshop, and Wings theater, as well as theaters in Philly, Ft. Lauderdale, Indianapolis, and Washington, DC. She is a Terra Nova Collective Groundbreakers Playwright Group alumni, a current member of Youngblood at the Ensemble Studio Theater, a founding member of Everywhere Theatre Group, and a former short-form resident artist at the Ontological Hysteric Theater. Her work has been featured in the *New York Times*, nytheatre.com, Broadway World, Culturebot, the *Miami Harold*, *Sun-Sentinel*, the

Guardian, and more. In addition to her plays, Leah's essays on biracial hapa identity were commissioned by the Japanese American National Museum's Discover Nikkei Project.

Bryan Zubalsky lives in the Hudson Valley New York, where he writes, bakes, gardens, and reads many sacred and philosophical books. Soon he will be moving elsewhere to pursue a first professional master's degree in Landscape Architecture. He hopes you found reading his poem a worthwhile way to spend some moments of your life. Be well and logic bless.

So...are you a grown-up?

☐ Yes

☐ No